THE FANTASY FACTOR

THE FANTASY FACTOR

USING YOUR IMAGINATION TO SOLVE
EVERYDAY PROBLEMS

H.E. STANTON

An OPTIMA book

© H.E. Stanton 1985

First published in Australia in 1985 by
Fontana Australia
This edition published in Great Britain in 1988 by
Macdonald Optima, a division of
Macdonald & Co. (Publishers) Ltd

A member of Maxwell Pergamon Publishing Corporation plc

British Library Cataloguing in Publication Data
Stanton, H.E. (Harry E.)
    The fantasy factor.
    1. Man. Stress. Self-treatment
    I. Title
    158.1

    ISBN 0-356-15193-X

Macdonald & Co. (Publishers) Ltd
3rd Floor
Greater London House
Hampstead Road
London NW1 7QX

Printed and bound in Great Britain at
The Guernsey Press

Dedication

To my family, a source of great imaginative delight

Acknowledgements

In addition to the sources I have quoted in the text, I would like to acknowledge my debt to family, patients, students and colleagues who have shared their fantasies with me and indicated how they have benefited from these. I would also like to express my thanks to Sylvia Murrell for her assistance in the preparation of the manuscript.

Contents

1 Introduction

You know more than you think you know

In a previous book, *The Healing Factor: a guide to positive health,* I suggested that it is not enough to continually gather knowledge about how we can live our lives more successfully. We already know how to do this. Our problem is that we do not *use* the information we have.

This may be due to laziness. It is far easier to talk about doing something or to think about doing something than it is to actually do it. However, it may also be due to the fact that often we simply do not *know* that we already have the information we need.

Use of a series of straightforward questions can make this clear. First, ask yourself the following two questions: 'what do I have now?' and 'what do I want?' If there is no difference between your answers to these two questions, then you have no difficulty. However, if there is a difference, the questions have helped you identify your problem. The next inquiry that you make is vital: 'what stops me getting what I want?' If a definite obstacle can be identified, you then ask: 'What do I need to do to overcome it?'

Clarified in this way, problems which were once seen as insoluble often become manageable as we realize that we have the resources necessary to achieve what we want. The questions enable us to cut through the fog that we so easily create around our difficulties, and to see clearly what is required. Of course, quite frequently, too, we find that the answer to the question 'What stops me?' is 'Nothing!' In other words, the only thing stopping me from getting what I want is myself, possibly through telling myself that I cannot do something even before I find out whether I really can do it or not.

A weightlifter with whom I worked several years ago illustrates the point. I will call this lad Gary Jones though that is not his real name. (Throughout this book I have followed this procedure of using fictitious names. This, of course, is to protect the anonymity of the real people involved in the actual cases.) Gary was at one time considered to be an Olympic Games medal prospect. However, for a period of over 19 months he seemed unable to improve his performance.

In our first session, I led Gary into imagining himself competing in an Australian championship. He saw the crowd, the platform, and his fellow contestants. He heard the buzz of conversation, the thumping of the weights onto the mat; he felt the bar in his hands and he even smelt the resin. Once Gary had placed himself in this situation, I suggested that he make his lift without consciously deciding what the weight would be. His unconscious mind would provide this information because it 'knew' what he was capable of, even if he did not seem to know this consciously. He would then, later, be able to go to the gymnasium and actually lift this weight.

So Gary imagined himself making the lift. He did not tell me what the weight was. Nor did I inquire. About an hour later, he rang to say that he had lifted 12 kilos more than he had ever done before. Obviously, Gary had been able to do this all the time. But he had mentally labelled the weight that he was normally lifting as his maximum, and he had mentally labelled any greater lift as impossible.

We do act in accordance with the things we tell ourselves. Another patient, Wendy Grant, was reluctant to actually sit down at her typewriter and produce the material necessary in her work as a journalist. She just 'didn't feel like it'. By telling herself this, she was blocking herself from taking action. What she eventually did was to imagine herself going to the typewriter, sitting down, placing her notes beside her and her hands on the keyboard, and producing the required material. Once she had imagined herself behaving in this way she had no difficulty in duplicating these 'actions' and actually doing the necessary work. So Wendy knew what to do all along.

So did Barry Turnbull, a third patient. While getting down a book from a high shelf in the library where he worked, Barry strained his back. I suggested that he use colour to accelerate the healing process. This would involve him thinking about the injured area and noting what colour it was. Then he would do the same for an uninjured area of his body, and mentally he would 'change' the injury colour to the healthy colour. Barry said that he could not imagine any colour at all for his injury. Yet when I said 'If there was a colour there, what would it be?' his reply was 'Oh, brownish'.

In all three cases, the people involved knew more than they thought they knew. Through the use of their imagination, they were able to tap into this deeper knowledge and use it to help themselves. That is what this book is about. It describes many ways in which you can use your imagination to solve problems that you may have felt were beyond you. I stress that *many ways* will be found within the pages of this book. There is not, I believe, a right way which must be followed by everyone. Simply try out the various techniques which appeal to you without putting any pressure on yourself. Impatience will not be helpful, nor will exhorting yourself to try harder. Just enjoy yourself and give your imagination free rein.

Be your own therapist

In a book entitled *The Mind Game,* Torrey reports on his

investigations into the therapeutic process as it is conducted in a number of different cultures. His conclusion is that four elements are always present in any successful helping relationship. The first of these is the sharing of a view of the world by both patient and therapist. This means that a label is put on whatever it is that is troubling the patient, one which he or she can readily accept. Once this is achieved, the first step in effecting a cure has been taken, for the offending agent has been identified. The interesting thing is that whether the label is actually correct or not seems to be irrelevant. It simply must make sense to the patient. Thus a witch doctor may label the problem as due to the presence of an evil spirit taking possession of the patient's soul, while a modern psychiatrist might apply the label of childhood trauma.

So naming the 'illness' helps to soothe and gratify the patient. Torrey's second factor makes the patient feel better, too. This is achieved through the therapist being warm, genuine, accepting, and able to see things from the patient's viewpoint. Such an attitude provides support and understanding.

Perhaps the most important of Torrey's four essential therapeutic components is the third. This involves the patient's belief and expectation. If a patient believes that someone or something can actually help him or her feel well, then that patient is already well on the way to a cure. That is, expecting positive outcome from therapy (an attitude which is encouraged by the therapist's belief in the techniques being used) creates a strong rapport between patient and therapist which contributes greatly to success. Improvement of our lives, therefore, comes from within ourselves, in terms of the way we choose to think about things.

The matter of techniques is Torrey's final point. Some form of healing ritual is necessary, although it does not matter particularly what it is so long as both patient and therapist believe that it will lead to a 'cure'. The witch doctor may lead his native client through an elaborate dance to banish the evil spirit. This usually works. However, it is unlikely to produce the same positive result with the modern Western patient who expects to receive insight into his problem through pouring out his childhood memories to the psychiatrist.

Realizing the importance of these four factors enables us to become our own therapists. You, the reader, provide the first three. To begin, you label your problem — anxiety, insomnia, lack of sexual interest, depression, pain, lack of energy, asthma, headaches, being overweight, smoking, nail-biting, or whatever. Secondly, you accept yourself and your problem as reasonable and normal. Blame, recrimination, and self-dislike are not useful. They just make you feel bad without providing any answers. Treat yourself as you would a guest in your home: courteously, warmly, and tolerantly. Be your own best friend, by providing encouragement and kind words for yourself. Thirdly, believe in your ability to help yourself, to draw on your inner strength to change these things in your life which you want to change.

In this way, you provide Torrey's first three factors. This book will provide the fourth — a healing ritual in terms of using the power of imagination. The mind can go anywhere, and do anything. It can transcend time, taking us back into the past or forward into the future. It can transcend space, taking us back into the past or forward into the future. It can transcend space, taking us to places both real and imaginary.

Our imagination is a very valuable tool, though it is two-edged. In *The Stress Factor*, I also pointed out how, frequently, we use our imagination in order to create great distress in our lives. We do this by anticipating troubles, and then reacting to them with a stress response which mobilizes our body for action. Such constant mobilization, with its flooding of our systems with adrenalin and other chemical substances, is a prime cause of illness. However, there *is* a very positive way in which our imagination may be used. And this is the other edge to the sword.

The positive value of imagination

Singer and Switzer express it well in their book, *Mind Play*, when they say:

> Your imagination, your capacity to daydream or fantasize, to relive the past or probe the future through pictures in your mind's eye, is one of the greatest resources you have as a human being. Wired into the natural functioning of your brain there is a powerful resource of healthy escape, for self-entertainment, and for fuller and more effective living. Don't be afraid to daydream or to use your imagination because you fear that you will lose touch with reality. You can learn to enjoy and to control the great powers of your imagination and from these inner resources you can often forge a better reality.

We have so much material stored in our heads, often considerably more than we think we have. This we can use as fantasies and daydreams to enrich our lives through entertaining, educating, changing and comforting ourselves. Though we may mentally play with fantasy to build a happier world for ourselves, there is usually no real danger that we will retreat into the world of delusion. The boundaries between fantasy and reality are easy to recognize as we shift back and forth at will. So, the real issue is whether we choose to dismiss daydreaming as a childish, useless pursuit, or whether we choose to use it in ways which will enrich our lives.

This book follows the latter course. It attempts to provide a guide to the positive use of imagination so that you will be able to enjoy your ability to make your life healthier, more interesting, and more creative without feeling guilty about mind-wandering. Why should you feel guilty, when fantasizing can produce these benefits as listed by Singer and Switzer?

- Reduction of stress
- Helping us plan a more effective future
- Gaining control over undesirable habits
- Helping us become more sensitive to the moods and needs of others
- Increasing our sexual pleasure
- Enhancing our creativity
- Learning more about ourselves
- Helping us amuse ourselves in idle moments
- Overcoming boredom
- Heightening our enjoyment of art, literature, music, theatre, and films
- Dealing more effectively with the loneliness of old age and enabling us to confront our own death with dignity.

Once we accept the value of daydreaming and fantasy in our lives, then we can deliberately set aside time for such activities. Although it is possible to allow our imagination free rein in many situations and under a wide variety of conditions, it is often useful to sit quietly, either with eyes open and focused on some object, or closed, and to simply allow memories, images and desires to drift gently through our minds.

The ease with which individuals become increasingly absorbed in this activity varies considerably from person to person. Relaxation, however, does appear to facilitate the production of mental images. In this state, we tend to withdraw attention from the external world and to focus on our own inner world. Interestingly enough, what we experience in imagery can be considered in many essential ways to be psychologically equivalent to experiencing the same thing in actuality. This is the basis of mental rehearsal for improving sporting performance, a topic to be discussed in a later chapter. Similarly, the person who wishes to lose weight can often do so by imagining being on a set of scales showing his or her desired weight. By continually visualizing in this way, particularly during periods of relaxation, the individual's mind comes to accept the desired weight as the 'reality' and does what is necessary to make it happen.

Images have great power to produce physiological change — as we shall see in the chapters dealing with healing and pain relief. People can increase their heart rate, for example, by reflecting on arousing images such as running hard or engaging in sexual activity. Other appropriate images can produce increases in blood glucose or in gastric acid secretion; yet others can lead to the formation of blisters, or to changes in skin temperature and even to a reduction in blood pressure.

Our imagination can also be useful in preventing us from behaving in ways that are not in our best interests. Marie Tate, for example, is a lady who used to be a shoplifter. She broke the habit by imagining any item that she was tempted to steal as being covered by a filthy, greenish slime which looked and smelt revolting. She would also imagine herself being arrested and kept in jail overnight, then appearing in court with all her relatives and friends witnessing her disgrace. In Marie's case, her imagination probably saved her from considerable embarrassment and hardship. Obviously, then, this ability is one which is worthy of development.

Improve your capacity to use your imagination

Even though it is virtually impossible to go through life without daydreaming, some people find it more difficult than others to use their imagination effectively. Often, such people have been taught early in their lives that fantasizing and daydreaming are useless and time-wasting activities which get in the way of the real business of life, as defined in terms of precise, rational and tightly-controlled thinking. Such thinking is of course valuable. So, too, is the looser, more imaginative, thinking. It is not a matter of either/or, but of using *both* forms effectively.

To improve your imaginative capacity, it is useful to begin with your dreams, both daytime and night-time. You may care to keep a record of those which you remember, replaying them a number of times in your mind. Keep a stock of pleasant ones available for the times when you may need a 'lift'. Of course, you may want to edit and change them to make them even more appealing. The idea is for you to become familiar with your imaginings, so that you are comfortable when using them to achieve specific goals. This involves practice.

Such practice can be with concrete objects as well as with your internal images. Look at a photograph in a magazine. Then fix your attention elsewhere, say on the ceiling or a blank wall. Reproduce that picture as clearly as you can. There is no need to try too hard. Just let the image form, almost by itself, without worrying about whether you are doing it well enough. Incidentally, this is a very productive way of using time while you are in waiting rooms where magazines are available. Paintings on the wall will also provide opportunities for you to practise in this way.

You may find that keeping your eyes open makes your task more difficult. If so, close them. It is often a lot easier when you do so, particularly if you are imagining movement. This is yet another way of developing your imaginative skills. Remember an event from your past, or else a favourite film or television show. Simply let it run through your mind. If you prefer to keep your eyes open, project it on the ceiling or the wall. You can then imagine yourself entering into the 'you' who is in your mental image and experiencing the appropriate feelings. As we shall see later, this is a very useful procedure in effecting behaviour change.

As you practise with both still and moving scenes, experiment to find how you might increase their vividness. Can you add sound? taste? smell? touch? Some people can. Others cannot. Are you able to make the colours bright, the details of dress sharp? It is very useful to practise doing these things; but, fortunately, even if your imagery remains fuzzy and ill-defined, you will still be able to achieve most of the benefits described in these pages.

One of the most valuable ways to develop your imaginative capacity is to picture scenes in which you might become involved in the future. Perhaps you are diffident about returning a malfunctioning electrical appliance to the store from which you purchased it. If so, visualize yourself taking the appliance into the store, explaining to the person who sold it to you what has happened, and requesting that he propose a solution satisfactory to you. You may run through several scenarios, trying out different approaches and behaviours, until you settle on the one that you feel is most likely to achieve the result you want. Be your own script writer. Rehearse your desired behaviour. Not only is this a marvellous way to improve your ability to imagine, but it also teaches you how to handle yourself more effectively in real-life situations. You learn in this way to prepare yourself, to calm yourself and to turn off worry, which are all valuable attributes in the living of an enjoyable life.

Injection of humour into such daydreaming helps, too. In the *Plus Factor*, I pointed out how you might reduce your awe of 'important' people and by so doing, reduce their control over you. Simply imagine them in some ridiculous situation. It is hard to be in awe of an overbearing boss if you imagine him with his trousers down around his ankles, or with several of his front teeth blacked out like an old-time comedian.

In *Psycheye*, Ahsen suggests that you develop your imaginative ability by:

- Repeated concentration on the selected image in your mind

- Experiencing the feeling associated with the picture over and over again
- Letting the meaning of the image come to mind in a spontaneous manner
- Interacting with the image in various ways, such as concentrating on its various details, noting people and objects present and asking questions of them
- Allowing the picture to progress so that the image spontaneously changes into something else
- Permitting mental expansion so that new experiences, insight, and change slowly emerge at many levels.

Another very valuable action which you can take to improve your imaginative ability is the creation of a suitable frame of mind. This is often referred to as a trance-like state, one in which the mind finds it easy to drift and dream. Trance is an everyday occurrence. Daydreaming, or else becoming so completely involved in a book, a film or a television programme that we fail to be aware of people talking to us, or highway amnesia (where we reach a destination without being aware of having passed through other towns on the way) are common examples. Trance is basically a state of inner absorption.

To a greater or lesser extent, everyone has this capacity to enter trance, and we may use this to help us achieve our goals. All that a trance state really involves is creating an internal world in our mind and 'turning off' the external world. We retain all our normal abilities in this internal world, but we can learn to gain more control over them. In particular, we can find out how to utilize the power of our unconscious mind to help us achieve the things that we want. The next chapter outlines how we might do this.

2 Contacting the Unconscious

Our unconscious mind

Whether it is actually true or not, it often seems as if we have two minds. One of these, our conscious mind, uses information supplied by our five senses and concerns itself with planning, thinking, and reasoning. The other, our unconscious mind, seems to operate independently of our senses, using some form of intuition as a means of gaining information. It appears to control our breathing, digestion, habits, emotions, and memory. I say 'appears to' because we have no hard scientific evidence for this entity. Nevertheless, use of the concept of an unconscious mind can be very valuable. If we 'act as if' we have such a mind, we can influence it to improve our life through the use of our imagination and reap rich rewards.

This idea of 'acting as if' something is true is important. We really do not, I believe, live in a world of external reality. Our reality is in our heads. Many of the principles by which we attempt to live are simply wrong, in that they make our lives more difficult than they need be. These principles, whatever they may be, are simply ways of organizing our experience; and the test of their usefulness really lies in the results that they produce. If, as a result of the principles and the beliefs which you hold, you are able to live your life in a way that is satisfying and rewarding, then you have organized your experience in an effective way. But if you do not achieve this positive result, perhaps it would be helpful to modify the way you see the world. Influencing your unconscious mind through the use of imagination can be one such modification.

Perhaps the most important aspect of the unconscious mind, which I shall now talk about as if it does actually exist, is its willingness to accept suggestion more readily and uncritically than does the conscious mind. This has both positive and negative aspects.

'Dumping' the rubbish

Joanne Ridings, a very talented and intelligent lady, certainly found this to be so. During a period when Joanne was ill, her mother, mother-in-law, and husband took advantage of her weakened state to bombard her with negative suggestions. Possibly, without realizing it, they were jealous of her business success and took this opportunity to assert their own 'superiority'. Be that as it may, Joanne remained in a state of depression even after she had recovered her physical health. She had unconsciously accepted much of the negative input. When we are ill, our minds frequently drift off into trance, and suggestions given at such a time have great impact. That was the case with Joanne.

Fortunately, the same method can be used to reverse the situation. Joanne used a trance state in which she imagined herself 'dumping' all the fears, doubt, anxieties, and guilts which had been generated by the negative input. She did this by visualizing herself going into her laundry, filling the sink with water, opening a trap door in her head, pulling out the unwanted rubbish and 'dumping' it in the water, which became blacker and blacker as she did so. Finally, she imagined pulling out the plug and letting the inky water vanish down the sink.

There are many other ways Joanne could have chosen to get rid of her 'mental rubbish'. She might have loaded it into a basket, attached the basket to a balloon, and let it drift away into the sky to finally vanish. Or perhaps she might have buried it, or burned it, and watched the smoke vanish up the chimney. We often keep negative thoughts, worries, fears, and resentments alive in our mind by continuing to think about them. But we do not have to. If we can choose to keep them in our mind, then we can also choose to get rid of them if we prefer to do so.

Geoff Bartley provides another example of how 'dumping' can achieve this end. Geoff was afraid to drive a car. Long before he contacted me (25 years before) he had been involved in an accident. Another motorist had run into the back of his car as he was waiting at a traffic light. Geoff received neck and spinal injuries, from which he fully recovered. However, from then on he would become extremely agitated whenever he saw another car behind him. This would occur even when he was a passenger. Whenever he would attempt to drive a car himself, the fear became so strong that he was virtually paralyzed.

The particular 'dumping' technique which I used with Geoff consisted of him imagining himself going into a corridor leading into his own mind. There he felt safe and comfortable. As he walked along the corridor he would come to a barrier with a 'Stop' sign on it. The sign had an arrow pointing to one of the corridor walls, with the words: 'Dump all rubbish here'. In the corridor wall there was a rubbish chute. I suggested to Geoff that he could get rid of anything he wanted down this chute. Anything that was in his life now which he did not want to keep could be 'dumped' down this chute to disappear out of his mind. And once it disappeared from his mind it would disappear from his life. Apparently, as we did this imaginative 'exercise' together, Geoff relived his accident, wrapped it up in a garbage bag, and got rid of it down the chute. He then went home and drove his wife's car.

Results are not always as spectacular. Sometimes it is necessary to dump mental 'rubbish' several times before it disappears. But disappear it usually will. All that is necessary is to find a particular way of 'dumping' that feels reasonable to you and to imagine yourself doing it.

Such images do appear to work as powerful influences on the memory storehouse of the unconscious mind, enabling it to let go of unwanted material. Though verbal suggestions can be very effective, mental images seem to exert a more powerful effect, particularly if they are used while in a trance state.

Entering a trance state

Trance is so much a part of everyday life that most people require little effort to drift into this state. Usually some point of concentration is required. Counting is a popular one. Count to 20, suggesting to yourself that at 5 your eyes will feel heavy; that at 10 the heaviness will increase to the point where they will want to close; that at 15, your eyes will close; and that at each count up to 20 they will feel heavier and heavier. At 20 you will be deeply relaxed, your mind calm and peaceful.

A variant on this method is to sit quietly with your eyes fixed on an object which is at some distance from you. Count from 1 to 10, letting your eyes close as you do, and synchronizing your count with your out-breath. At 10, reverse the count going back down to 1. At this point, open your eyes, fixing your gaze on the object again. Count to 10 once more, letting go to a greater extent with each count. At 10 you will probably feel pleasantly entranced. If not, repeat the procedure until you do.

Perhaps you may prefer to link numbers and imagery. Then just imagine whiteness everywhere you look. As you count from 10 to 0, see the numbers against this white background. At first they will be sharp, distinct and black, but, as the counting continues, they become increasingly vague and fuzzy, difficult to see clearly, fading away into the whiteness. When you reach 0, there is nothing, just blankness, whiteness.

Zeros are very useful for trance induction. You can relax and let things take care of themselves. Go limp and let everything drift away. Think of a big, black round 0 — it's a zero, it's nothing. You're thinking of nothing until your mind is a blank. It becomes like a big white wall with nothing on it, just white wherever you look except for the big, black 0, which is gradually fading away into the white wall, becoming invisible, becoming nothing. When it does, you will have developed a comfortable trance. Often this is quicker than counting down from 10.

Using a mental blackboard can also be helpful. Visualize a blackboard in your mind; and, on it, draw a large circle. Decide on the end point that you want to use (10, 20, 30 or whatever) and simply imagine yourself drawing the number 1 in the centre of the circle. Mentally erase it carefully, leaving the circle intact, and write the number 2. Continue doing so until you reach the end point which you have previously told yourself will signal your entry into trance. Allow yourself to let go a little more with each number you draw in the circle. Letters of the alphabet work just as well if you prefer to use them rather than numbers.

Images can also induce a trance state. Sit quietly, breathing evenly and regularly, and tell yourself that an image, which is able to be described in just one word, will spontaneously drift into your mind. This image will be one that is effective for you as a means of creating a trance. In future, all you will need to do, is say the word three times, close your eyes, see the image in your mind, and let it lead you into deep mental relaxation.

Some images do seem more popular than others. Visualizing calm still water is one. Thinking of a black curtain which blots out everything else is another. Falling leaves are pleasant too. Just imagine yourself as a leaf on top of a tree. A gentle breeze detaches you so that you drift slowly to earth. You can set your own pace, allowing yourself to enter trance as the leaf drifts earthwards.

Even gazing at your own hand as if you were a sculptor or artist can provide an excellent entry into the relaxed mind-state. Concentrate on your hand as if you were going to sculpt or paint it, noting every little detail. Gradually the background behind your hand fades away, your eyelids become heavier, and you allow your body to let go. I've used the word 'allow' deliberately, for that is the key to creating a trance state. You let it happen rather than try to make it happen.

Sometimes this is easier to achieve with more active trance-induction methods. One of these involves extending your arm at shoulder level with a slight turn so you can see your thumb nail. Fix your gaze on the nail. Concentrate intently as it seems to become bigger and bigger, filling your entire visual field. As the nail appears to grow in size, bend your arm very, very slowly, bringing your hand ever closer to your face. Allow your eyes to become increasingly heavy as this occurs so that, when your hand or fingers touch your face, your eyes close naturally, your hand flops down onto your lap, and you are in a comfortable trance.

Another method is a matter of rolling your eyes upward as if attempting to look at the top of your head. Hold this position as you take a deep breath. Allow your eyelids to close over your upward-looking eyes, and finally let your breath go while relaxing your eyes, and experiencing a sensation of floating. This feeling of lightness may be concentrated in your right hand and forearm (or left, if you are left-handed) so that it floats upwards to an upright position. There is nothing particularly unusual about generating this sort of arm movement, for our mind does control our body. If we think 'light', 'floating', our arm will normally obey our mental commands.

Use of imagery can assist the process. You can imagine, for example, that your forearm is a feather floating upwards, or that a string attached to a balloon has encircled your wrist and is drawing it upwards as the balloon floats higher into the air. On the other hand, you may prefer to begin with one arm held straight out in front of you, palm upwards, as you imagine that you are holding an empty bucket in that hand. Sand is pouring into this bucket, so that it becomes heavier and heavier, pulling your arm lower and lower. As your arm comes down, allow yourself to let go more and more so that when it touches your lap you can relax completely.

Obviously, there are countless ways of helping yourself to enter a trance state. It is a matter of selecting those with which you feel comfortable and which create, for you, a pleasant state of mental and physical relaxation. Calm people, who are already rather relaxed, often prefer the non-action methods; while nervous, more highly strung people may experience greater success with active approaches. For many of us, all that is necessary is to engage in our favourite daydream.

Deepening the trance

Once you have become used to the idea that you can drift in and out of trance at will, you may wish to experiment with your ability to deepen your trance so as to find if this will help you in the use of your imagination. As with induction techniques, this is also a question of selection, of your being able to find a way of helping yourself to let go more completely. Usually this can be achieved by simply taking more time over doing the things that I have already suggested, or else by combining a number of them.

An acquaintance of mine, Bill Thompson, begins with 'following his breath'. He simply concentrates on his breath as it flows in and out, never attempting to change it in any way, but just flowing with it. Interestingly enough, when Bill focuses consciously on his breathing in this way, his unconscious mind appears to do whatever is necessary to facilitate his relaxation. Thus his blood pressure drops a little, his heart rate slows, his breathing also slows and becomes deeper, and he is increasingly aware of a sense of comfort and ease spreading throughout his body.

This is the second aspect of Bill's technique — concentrating upon relaxing his muscles. Initially he did so by alternately tensing and relaxing each muscle group in turn, beginning with his feet and finishing with his forehead. However, he has now become so adept that he simply imagines his muscle tension flowing away simultaneously with his breath as he lets it go.

Once he feels that his muscles are relaxed, Bill calms his mind by thinking of some pleasant scene, any place where he feels peaceful and content. Finally, he counts slowly from 1 to 20. By the time he reaches 20 he is already in the state which he has decided is best for increasing the power of his imagination.

Probably, the use of additional imagery is the most common form of deepening. You can imagine a beautiful bush setting, with you sitting beside a stream surrounded by fallen leaves. Idly, you pick up a leaf, drop it into the stream and watch it float gently downstream, bobbing and drifting. The leaf takes your mind deeper into trance as it moves further away to finally disappear. You can use as many leaves as you wish to create the state of mind that you desire.

Perhaps you like beaches. Many of us do. They provide marvellous opportunities to involve all our senses in our imaginings. You can visualize yourself, then, lying on this glorious beach. The sand is clean and white, the water is blue, and the waves are frothing on the sand. Perhaps you can hear the cries of the gulls, the gentle lapping of the waves. There is the smell of salt, and the feeling of warmth as the sun's rays soak into your body. Your imagination can embellish such a scene as much as you wish. You may feel the breeze on your cheek, the sand beneath your feet as you walk towards the water, the coolness of this water as you begin to swim. Let the water caress you or exhilarate you as you wish, for you may use your imagery to create any mood you desire. It is all a matter of becoming intensely absorbed in your imaginings. By doing so you create a mental state which enables you to make your trance much deeper.

If the great outdoors does not appeal to you, use a more domestic image to carry you deeper. A popular one, if you do not feel uncomfortable in lifts, is to imagine that you are on, say, the tenth floor of a building. Here you are, waiting in the carpeted hallway for the lift to take you to ground level. When the lift arrives you enter, turning to face the front as the doors close. Gaze at the indicator showing the floor numbers. The number 10 is illuminated. As the lift descends smoothly, effortlessly and without interruption (because this is your own lift which no one else will use) the numbers 9,8,7,6,5,4,3,2,1,G successively light up. Your mental state gets deeper and deeper with each illuminated number. By the time ground level is reached, you can feel a wondrous sense of tranquility, and this may be increased by continuing the exercise.

Imagine the lift doors opening. You pass through them and enter a door opposite. This is your special place, a place where no one or nothing can harm or damage you in any way. It can be anywhere — outside (a garden, a beach, a river bank) or inside (a beautiful room, a comfortable bed, a warm bath). Perhaps it could be a place from your past, a place that you really enjoyed as a child, or perhaps it is pure fantasy and not a real place at all. You need not create it consciously, for, if you let it, your unconscious mind itself will provide such a place for you. This place is somewhere where you can get in touch with your unconscious mind, and let it solve your problems for you.

Using suggestion

In that special place of yours, your mind will be very receptive to the suggestions which you can give yourself — regardless of whether these are words, images, or a combination of the two. As it appears that the unconscious mind does not reason, simple suggestions are usually best, particularly if they are repeated at frequent intervals. As Leslie Wetherhead has put in his book, *Psychology, Religion, and Healing:*

Behind all the discoveries of psychologists since Mesmer ... lies one of the great truths about the mind ... If the mind really accepts an idea as true, and if the idea is reasonable, it tends by means of unconscious processes, to actualize itself or come true. To bring about the entry of an integrating idea into the mind, so that the idea may 'come true'... is called treatment by suggestion.

Usually we regard treatment by suggestion as something that one person does to another. In fact we do not need someone else. We usually know what we want, so we can easily provide our own suggestions. After all, if somebody else gives you a suggestion, first your own mind has to accept it before it can be of any value to you. That is, we always have to translate the input of others into suggestions to ourselves. This is exactly what Joanne Ridings did. She accepted the negative suggestions of her family and made them into her own, by telling herself the same things. Other people can only exert their influence over us if we cooperate with them, precisely by translating their suggestions into self-suggestions.

Joanne, in fact, used a particular mental image to prevent this from ever happening in the future. She imagined herself putting on a beautiful golden helmet and then closing the visor. Within this helmet she was safe from the negative influences of others. Their damaging suggestions could not penetrate her protection, and she actually imagined these bouncing off the helmet. When the spate of negative input would dry up, she would remove her headpiece. A simple, but very effective, image, it is worth keeping in mind. For unfortunately most of us are surrounded by nay-sayers, people who are negative themselves and resent positive thinking in others.

An image such as the helmet provides protection. Other images can be symbols of confidence and power. Bill Thompson makes use of one which he feels has helped him immensely in coping with difficult tasks. His special place is a beautiful garden. In it is a tree — strong, straight and tall. He notices the depth and strength of its root system, the security that it offers to nesting birds through the spread of its branches, the energy that it gains from the sun as it reaches upwards. Bill compares himself to that tree in that he is firmly grounded, strong and secure, not just providing strength to others but also reaching out to gain strength from his surroundings. Though he shares many of the tree's attributes, Bill realizes that he is even more powerful because he has the capacity to think, to reason, and to choose to take more control of his life.

Whenever he doubts his ability to handle a task or a problem, Bill then imagines that tree and, as he does, he experiences a surge of power and confidence within him. Although suggestions given in words can be quite helpful, it seems that images are the language of the unconscious. By using his tree as a symbol of self-confidence, Bill is tapping into very powerful forces. The next chapter provides many more examples of how we can tap into our unconscious potential.

3 Tapping Unconscious Potentialities

A 'special' place

To make contact with the unconscious mind so that I can make use of its tremendous resources, I use a strategy similar to that of Bill Thompson. I begin with an image of blackness. A black velvet curtain comes down in my mind and blots out everything else. Then I let my out-breath take away all tension, discomfort, and unwanted feelings. Next, I use the 'dumping' technique that I have described when talking about Geoff Bartley's fear of driving. Anything bothering me goes down the chute. Finally, I mentally go into my 'special' place, experiencing deep contentment and tranquility.

Sometimes, I will simply rest in this state, turning off the world for a while. This can be immensely valuable in that I can let go of all tensions and pressures. On other occasions I will use the 'special' place to achieve some particular purpose that I have in mind, a purpose best attained through the use of unconscious mental processes. These processes will be discussed in the pages that follow; but, before I do so, I would like to add a little to this concept of a 'special' place.

It can be very useful to carry in your mind a place into which you can go and shut the door on the rest of the world. I'm not suggesting, of course, that you do this so frequently that you live only in your own private world, separated from the rest of humanity. Rather, I would like you to entertain the thought of using it so as to give yourself an occasional respite from a noisy, pressure-laden world. See it as an oasis of peace and quiet, an opportunity to still the seemingly endless babble of your mind, and an opportunity to stimulate beneficial changes in yourself.

Though I prefer to let the unconscious mind provide a 'special' place, you on the other hand may wish to construct it quite consciously and deliberately. This could involve finding a favourite spot and building a one-room centre. In *The Book of EST,* Rhinehart suggests that you choose your own materials and pantomime the actual building process with your hands. Inside the centre which you construct, you can provide a desk and two chairs, a magic wish-button, a television screen, a digital clock which enables you to view any event at any time in the past, a stage where you can bring people to life, and an 'abilities' cabinet where you can hang the suits which, when donned, give you mastery of any ability you would like to have.

Perhaps you may not wish to enter into such an elaborate fantasy as the one suggested by Rhinehart. In that case, just think of your 'special' place as somewhere you can enter and shut a door on all your worries, tensions, and pain. These are left outside. This place is absolutely perfect. It has been designed for your pleasure, satisfaction, comfort, and security. Nothing or no one can enter without your permission. This 'special' place concept when combined with that of 'dumping' is a very powerful way of using your imagination to tap unconscious potentials.

Some additional 'dumping' techniques

Because I feel that the idea of 'dumping' worries, tensions, and discomfort is so important, I would like to suggest additional fantasies which may help you eliminate these from your life. These combine quite easily with your 'special' place.

Joan Hart, the wife of a colleague of mine, has as her

'special' place a beautifully furnished room with a deep-pile carpet and superb drapes. In this room is a large freestone fireplace. Joan enjoys imagining herself standing or sitting in front of the fire, seeing the flames and burning logs. She hears the crackle and hiss as the fire burns, she feels the warmth as its heat soaks into her body, and she smells the smoke. Should there be things that she wants to 'dump' — such as guilt, hostility, resentment, fear, or doubt — then she imagines them lying on a small table, in the form of accounts which have been paid. As there is no longer a need to keep these settled accounts around, she can then pick up these unnecessary papers and drop them into the fire, one by one. As each one turns to ashes and disappears in smoke up the chimney, Joan experiences a sense of release, a feeling which can be quite euphoric.

Her friend, Margaret Broadham, also uses a room as her 'special' place. In it she has a blackboard covering part of one wall. Should something be bothering her, she reduces the source of her anxiety to a few words, writes them on the blackboard, and then uses an eraser to remove them completely so that only blackness remains. Margaret thus wipes them out of her mind.

Should you have somewhere outside as your 'special' place, you might prefer to use the sky as a means of removing unwanted 'rubbish' from your mind. As you imagine the clear blue sky above you, you notice a dark cloud marring its perfection. This is your 'rubbish'. Watch this cloud as it floats away into the distance, becoming smaller and smaller, fading away into insignificance so that you hardly notice it at all. Or you may allow it to disappear completely if this is your wish.

Another helpful approach is to imagine yourself, inside your 'special' place if you wish, with an actual filing cabinet in your stomach. Feel yourself reaching into this cabinet and taking out one of the drawers holding a number of files. Imagine yourself flicking through these files, selecting some for removal because they are now finished business or because they are no longer a part of the more positive character that you are developing. These unwanted files may be destroyed, perhaps by burning them or by throwing them out as garbage.

Communicating with the unconscious mind

Sometimes it may be counter-productive to let things go because we need to make a definite decision. Yet, even here, it is often more effective to draw on our unconscious resources rather than to attempt to arrive at solutions through conscious means alone. In *The Plus Factor* I have described the method of unconscious problem-solving in some detail, so I shall not repeat it here — except to comment that the main point is to consciously review all the information you have, and then, without attempting to make a decision, to put it aside and do something else completely unrelated to the problem. At a later time, come back to the issue again. You'll find that you have produced more information in the time that you have not been consciously occupied with it. Put it from your mind again. Come back to it, and continue the process until your decision is virtually made for you. Just keep your conscious mind from interfering by deliberately turning it to other matters and you will get the answers you need. If this process seems rather long-winded, you may wish to attempt more direct communication with your unconscious mind.

In both *The Plus Factor* and *The Healing Factor*, I have explained how a pendulum may be used to communicate with the unconscious mind. Another way of achieving such communication is through ideomotor signals. We know that people are able to talk to each other through sign language. Probably the most common of all sign language is when you nod your head to signify 'yes' or shake it to indicate 'no'. On other occasions we say 'Yes, come here' by using a beckoning forefinger, or 'No, don't stay' by waving someone away with our hand. Although we do this frequently, saying 'yes' or 'no' through movements of our head, our hand, or our finger, yet we may not always be conscious of doing so. In other words, such signals, termed ideomotor, can be seen as unconscious movements. We may use this information to help us get in touch with our unconscious minds.

Relax yourself by any method which you have found effective, deepening this into a trance state if you wish. Ask your unconscious mind a question which can be answered with a simple 'yes' or 'no'. Make this a question to which your conscious mind does not know the answer. Only your unconscious mind knows the answer, and it will have to provide either a 'yes' or a 'no'. This it may do through a nod or shake of the head, a lifting of a finger or thumb, a movement of a hand, or something else. Interestingly enough, the signal may not be a physical movement but an internal sensation. My own communication may be either a lifting of the right index finger for 'yes' or of the left index finger for 'no', or just a sensation as if my head was nodding for 'yes' or shaking for 'no'. Yet, in this latter case, no actual movement takes place. The feeling is unmistakable, nevertheless.

If you have not used such a means of communication before, when you get your first answering signal, you will need to ask your unconscious if this is a 'yes' signal. Ask for a repeat if it is. If you get nothing, ask if it is a 'no' signal by requesting a repeat. In this way you establish the meaning of the ideomotor movements that your unconscious mind is providing. Possession of this means of communication can be very valuable in helping you acquire previously unavailable information. It also assists you to make more beneficial use of your unconscious mind. There are other ways of doing so, too.

Changing your personal history

As developed by Richard Bandler and John Grinder in their book *Frogs into Princes*, this technique is normally employed by a therapist to help patients change events in their past so they can handle their present more successfully. However, by a slight modification of the three basic steps, it is possible to adapt the approach so that a person can use it without the assistance of a therapist.

The first of these steps is to identify the behaviour which you wish to change, and to recreate, through the use of your imagination, the unpleasant feelings which are associated with this unwanted pattern. It may be helpful to let a colour drift into your mind as you do so, a colour associated with the negative feelings, which are then 'anchored'. This means that they are linked to some signal such as touching your left elbow with your right index finger. Thus unpleasant feelings, a colour, and a particular touch are now closely associated.

Secondly, you explore your experience to discover what resource you now possess which could be 'taken back' into the past to change the negative feelings. If, for example, you are often nervous and ill-at-ease when meeting strangers, you may realize that you now possess techniques for relaxing yourself which you did not have when you first experienced this nervousness. One way of identifying such resources is to think of a relatively recent experience which you handled in a relaxed, comfortable way. Should you be unable to find a resource which, if applied to the original, unpleasant situation, would have produced a more acceptable outcome, imagine how someone else whom you admire would have handled the situation. Normally, this use of a model is not required and you can enjoy thinking about your own use of the resource.

As you reflect on this successful experience and as you enjoy the positive feelings involved, allow a different colour to become associated with it. Also, use a different 'anchor', such as touching your left foot with your right foot. This completes the second step.

Finally, touch your first 'anchor' to recreate the

unpleasant feelings of the unwanted behaviour, while having the negative colour in your mind. As you experience this, touch your second 'anchor' while bringing in the positive feelings and colour of the resource. Keep touching both 'anchors', resting quietly for as long as it takes for the unpleasant feelings to change under the influence of the positive resource.

The process may then be generalized to any similar situations that you are likely to meet in the future. Just say to yourself: 'In future, anytime I experience any nervousness or agitation when meeting strangers at a party, I will feel calm and relaxed as I think of my positive colour and as I touch my left foot with my right.'

Change can be quite dramatic through the use of this technique, probably because it takes place at the unconscious rather than the conscious level. This is true, too, of another method — reframing, which is described by Bandler and Grinder.

Reframing

The basic concept of this approach is that you can communicate with the part of the mind which is responsible for the behaviour which you wish to change. The idea is that we all have different parts within us which want to do different things. Instead of being a single 'I', we are made up of a lot of little 'I's which often pull us in different directions. For example, one part of us may want to overeat because it loves food, while another part may wish to lose weight, and yet a third part may want to put on weight as a protection against extra-marital sexual involvement. It is almost as if we are multiple personalities with different parts causing us to behave in ways we do not understand. However, although we may not understand why we do act in certain ways, we are aware of our behaviour, and this distinguishes us from the 'true' multiple personality case — who has no such awareness.

Once you can accept this idea, namely that there are

different parts operating within you controlling various aspects of your behaviour, then you can use the reframing technique. Step 1 involves identification of the particular pattern of behaviour which you wish to change. This could be, for example, excessive shyness, overeating or over-aggressiveness. This pattern you can label X.

Communication with the part responsible for behaviour X is then initiated as step 2 with the question: 'Will that part of me that runs behaviour X communicate with me in consciousness?' Usually some ideomotor signal — a nod, finger lift, hand movement, or 'sensation' such as a tingle or a sense of internal excitement — will be forthcoming. The meaning of the signal is clarified by asking the responsible part to repeat it if it means 'yes'. Once this positive response is clearly identified, a 'no' reply is established in a similar fashion.

A distinction is then made between the actual behaviour, pattern X, and the purpose which the part hopes to achieve through that behaviour. The question is asked: 'Would you be willing to let me know in consciousness what you are trying to do for me by pattern X?' Sometimes a 'yes' response eventuates, and the part is then asked to go ahead and communicate its purpose by permitting it to just 'pop into' the mind. On other occasions, a 'no' reply is forthcoming, indicating the desire of the part to keep its intention from the conscious mind.

The next step in the reframing process involves the creation of new alternative behaviours which are beneficial to you while still achieving the part's purpose. It is assumed at this point that the part's intention is commendable but that the means which it is using to achieve its goal are no longer in your best interests. These alternative means are generated by asking the part responsible for pattern X to cooperate with the creative part of you to provide new behaviours capable of achieving its purpose, thus enabling pattern X to disappear as being no longer necessary. It is suggested that a 'yes' signal will be given as each new alternative is generated. Usually an arbitrary limit, say three, is imposed.

When the three signals have been given, the part responsible for the unwanted behaviour is asked: 'Are you willing to take responsibility for generating these (three) new alternatives when appropriate, so that pattern X may disappear?' Should the response be 'no', it could be suggested that the new behaviours be given a trial for a limited period, perhaps several weeks, and this usually produces a 'yes' answer. It is then suggested that if this trial proves successful, the new behaviour could become permanent.

A final check is made to ensure that no other part objects to the new alternatives. The question used is: 'Is there any other part of me that objects to the (three) new alternatives?' Should a 'yes' response be given, it is necessary to backtrack and replace the objected-to behaviours with further alternatives.

Although there is a temptation to regard such a process as nonsensical in that there may not be any such thing as your different parts, it is interesting to note that most people have no trouble at all in accepting the concept. It seems a reasonable explanation for much of their previously inexplicable behaviour. True, the explanation might be quite wrong; yet, if it provides the framework within which a successful ritual of change can be used, it serves its purpose. After all, most of us talk to ourselves rather frequently. Using the reframing approach, we can talk to ourselves with the definite purpose of promoting change which we think is desirable.

Drawing on past experience

The reframing technique is rather directive in that we are asking definite questions and receiving answers. It is a very structured situation. You may prefer a 'looser' way of going about gaining help from your unconscious mind.

One of the easiest and most effective of these is

illustrated by a session that I had with Don Hansen, an insurance salesman. Normally one of the nation's top sellers of life insurance policies, Don had been well down on his sales for over a year. In fact, the number of policies that he had written was almost 50% down on the average which he had maintained for the previous four years. Obviously Don had the resources within himself to perform much better than he was doing at present. What he now required was to be able to get in touch with these inner resources again.

I established the conditions under which Don could enter a trance state. He did this by focusing on his breathing, and letting his out-breath carry all tightness from his body. He then allowed his mind to drift in the direction of a pleasant memory.

I utilized this state by telling Don that, as he let go, resting comfortably and at peace, he would be able to enter the stillness of his inner mind and find himself in a place both beautiful and pleasing. There he would feel himself making contact with his deepest, innermost self and with the tremendous power of his unconscious mind. Thus he would rediscover those inner resources capable of stimulating any changes which he wanted.

I did not specify what these resources were — only that he possessed within himself the power to effect the desired changes, and that his unconscious mind would be able to do whatever was necessary to select the appropriate resource.

I compared Don's unconscious mind to a computer containing in its memory banks everything that had ever happened to him in his entire life. From this memory bank his unconscious mind would locate a very important experience — one which involved change, new learning, and success. This experience from his past life would be studied thoroughly by his unconscious mind in terms of images, sounds, and feelings. Through this thorough re-examination of an important past experience, Don's unconscious mind would learn something new and would gain fresh understanding of what was necessary for him to change. Using this new information, it would then do whatever was necessary for him to change in the way that he desired.

I made no attempt to tell Don which experience to select, or when he should use the experience, or to what end he should use it. These details were left to his unconscious mind. Don was simply told that he had within himself the resources that he needed to be able to change; and that by going through the process which I have been describing, he would be able to solve his problem.

Solve it he did. Within three months, the number of policies Don wrote increased markedly. From that point he never looked back, consistently producing a performance comparable to, or better than, that of previous years. He resumed his place as a top seller of life insurance.

You can use this method too. Establish a trance condition, assume that your unconscious mind has the resources which you need to achieve your desired outcome, and tell it to find an appropriate experience from your past — when you were able to change in some beneficial way. Ask it to revive and study this experience, learning whatever is required for change to take place, and to then do everything necessary for the desired outcome to be achieved.

This technique will produce change. So, too, will all the others that are outlined in this chapter — perhaps not every time and for every person, but sufficiently often to make their use well worthwhile. You are in control of the situation by deciding on the change that you want, although it is your unconscious mind which finds ways of carrying out your wishes. Sometimes, of course, you may have difficulty in deciding just what changes you do want to make in your life. Under such circumstances, other methods which are oriented towards helping you learn more about yourself are likely to be helpful.

4 Learning More About Yourself

Using your daydreams

Marie Castle is a very successful real estate saleswoman. She and her husband have postponed having children because of Marie's desire to prove herself in the business world. But Marie also daydreams a lot about homemaking, cooking, sewing, looking after babies. Though she perceives herself as competent, practical and hard-driving, in her daydreams she is softer and more caring.

Bob Coglan is the reverse. Mild-mannered and unassertive, he performs his duties as a clerk unobtrusively and quietly. In his daydreams, however, he is adventurous, dominant, and a leader of men.

Many of us have such daydreams; and they do not necessarily indicate that we want to be drastically different from the way we are. What they can do is indicate aspects of our personality which we tend to keep hidden, and which may serve us better if they are given more open expression. Even though we consciously think that we should be quite satisfied with our lives as they are, we may unconsciously be yearning for something else. This is particularly so if our daydreams seem to run completely opposite to our life experiences. Such a conflict would suggest that we are overlooking important aspects of our personality.

Giving expression to these aspects need not lead to vast changes in our lives. Bob could simply choose to become more assertive and forthright in his normal day-to-day interactions. On the other hand, he might also seek a new job which would give him increased scope to be adventurous. Marie could moderate her normal hard-driving efficiency, becoming gentler and less aggressive. Or she could go a lot further by giving up her job, perhaps only temporarily, while she has a family.

Our daydreams are more conscious and controllable than night dreams. They are far easier to remember, and so they are a useful source of information about our inner potentialities. This does not mean that the information which they provide must be followed; it only means that such information provides input which, taken together with other knowledge that we have, may indicate to us how we might make ourselves more 'complete'.

It would probably be a mistake to take daydreams too literally. If you have persistent daydreams about strangling a co-worker, it does not mean that you really want to murder him. However, it does suggest that you have a serious problem. If you cannot solve this, it may be desirable to explore ways in which it would be no longer necessary for you to work with him. That is, daydreams can be seen as indicators or guides to possible modifications in your life which would make it more enjoyable.

Daydreams actually seem to fall into patterns. Probably the most common is the positive, happy daydream, the one in which we indulge in pleasant, wishful thinking. In it, we achieve great things, assume special powers, win vast amounts of money, become devastatingly attractive, and generally enjoy ourselves. This is fun. Such daydreaming can be very helpful, too, in adding variety to our lives and assisting us to relax. We simply feel happier.

This is not the case with another pattern, especially if it becomes too prevalent. This involves guilty daydreams. At times we all have such daydreams. We feel bad about something that we have done or not done. That is reasonable enough. However, if we spend a lot of time daydreaming in such a way, we are likely to feel very miserable and depressed. Daydreaming about getting even for real or imagined slights, together with fantasies of hostility and revenge can, in moderation, be a useful escape valve, a way of letting off steam. But, if much of our daydreaming is concerned with guilt, hostility, aggression, and other negative emotions, it suggests that changes in our life may be necessary.

This is probably true, too, of a third pattern: mind-wandering. Again, at times we all experience this. Our thoughts seem to drift from one thing to another, never settling. Though we may decide to focus on our particular thing, we find ourselves unable to do so. Our daydreams are fragmented. Sometimes this mind-wandering becomes our predominant daydreaming pattern. If this is true of you, it is an indication that you might do well to learn more about yourself in an effort to locate troublesome areas in your life.

Spontaneous imagery

Your imagination can help you do this. Allow images to arise in your mind and interact with them. Just close your eyes, let an image drift into your mind, and talk to it. Then, become the image and let it talk back to you. This is an excellent way of also finding out the meanings of your night-time dreams. In turn, become all the objects and people in your dream. Usually the point of your dream becomes quickly apparent.

Returning to the spontaneously arising image, you might be able to change it once you ascertain its meaning. Bob Coglan, to whom I referred earlier, was quite capable of doing this. On one occasion, when he was feeling rather anxious about a work situation, Bob closed his eyes and described in words how he was feeling. He then waited for an image embodying that feeling to arrive. Arrive it did — a picture of a soft lump of clay. It was virtually shapeless. Bob interpreted this as meaning that he felt weak and helpless inside, unable to project any definite image to others. Fortunately, he did not leave it that way. He shaped the clay into the figure of a man in action, put it into a kiln, and baked it into a definite form. Bob gave himself a changed self-image which was gradually translated into changes in his behaviour.

Bob deliberately changed his image. Marie, the real estate saleswoman, did not. She began with a spontaneous picture, a diamond, brilliant and hard. This she contemplated, simply observing it as it began to unfold. She did not try to make it do anything, but just observed what changes occurred.

Any mental picture which you observe in this way will alter sooner or later. But be patient. Let it happen in its own time, without you impatiently jumping from one thing to another. Hold fast to your starting image, wait until it changes by itself, then ask it what the alterations mean. Positive changes may be retained, and negative ones allowed to pass, for soon further alteration will take place.

In Marie's case, the image change which she kept was that of a warm glow beginning as a yellow pinpoint deep in the diamond. This gradually expanded until the stone glowed with a warmth and vitality which was originally lacking. As it did so, the hard edges melted into softly flowing curves. Marie made no effort to retain an earlier alteration, which had the diamond cutting deep designs into a pane of glass. She simply exercised choice over the change which she wished to keep. It is, of course, possible to be more directive than this, deliberately stimulating the imagination to provide more information.

Of doors, windows, and animals

A door is a useful starting image. Imagine a door in a high wall or in a house. On it visualize a word such as 'love', 'hope', 'anxiety', 'guilt', or any other word relating to whatever it is that is currently concerning you. Open the door. Observe what lies behind it and let the process proceed spontaneously.

You might like to use three doors instead, all unlabelled. Enter each in turn. Interestingly enough, the image behind the middle door usually seems to indicate something about sexual or romantic relationships, although it may not make explicit reference to sex. One male acquaintance of mine found a roll of tangled barbed wire when he opened this middle door. The meaning that he attached to it was that his relationships were invariably prickly and complicated.

Of the two remaining doors, one will probably call forth an image relating to the way in which you interact with the outer world. Are you competitive? unaggressive? a loner? desperately seeking social acceptance? The image that you find there could well give you insight into your social and work life. The third door will possibly provide some insight into your self-image. It will reveal something of your inner life.

The use of three things is reflected in other starting images, too. Windows may be used instead of doors. You imagine yourself standing in a room in which there are three windows. One of these represents the past, another the present, and the third the future. Simply look through each window in turn. Whatever you see will usually relate to some difficulty that you may be experiencing in your life. You can then deliberately change the image to resolve this satisfactorily. You may want to alter the past so as to influence the present, which in turn creates a bright future.

Perhaps, as Arthur Phillips suggests in *Transformational Psychology*, you can use the trilogy concept to change your lifestyle. The patient is asked to close his eyes and think of himself being in a theatre that has three movie screens. He is to imagine that the projectionist runs his entire life on one of the screens, from the very beginning to the present moment, in superfast motion. Next, using his creativity and sense of humour as well as his deepest wishes, he is to allow the projectionist to project an alternative life on one of the other screens, one that he wishes he could have. After he does so, he is told that he can have one more chance to really create a totally different history for himself, in case he has been too tentative the first time. This could be on the third screen.

Once this has been completed, the patient, still in the theatre, would be able to see the three films run simultaneously on the three screens. He could shift his attention between screens at will. He would have to be very attentive, however, because the projectionist would insert, at random, in the midst of these 'lives', cartoons and comedy clips. Once this simultaneous showing is over, the patient then asks himself: 'Does it really matter which of the three lives was the actual one?'

You may like to try this fantasy for yourself. It could have the result of 'loosening up' some of your ideas about your lifestyle and permit wider choices. This same effect might also be achieved through an image of two animals. Imagine two different animals. Decide on the best word to describe each, and see them walking down a road together. Let the scene develop. Have one animal say something to the other. The second one answers. Reverse the procedure so that the animal who first answered now asks the question and the other one replies. As you watch this interplay, make a note of your feelings and emotions. Shorr, who developed this image and described it in his book *Psycho-imagination Therapy*, suggests that the intensity of feeling which is associated with the images may indicate the strength of a conflict; or else it may make you aware of a previously unrecognized conflict and of its importance in your life.

That is, the image of the two animals is a means of demonstrating one of the different ways in which conflict is expressed. Often they represent two opposing parts of ourselves, or an opposition between ourselves and some other person. At other times, it may be that a new way of behaving which we have adopted is in conflict with an older, more established, behavioural mode. An example given by Shorr clarifies the way in which the two-animals image may help you. The questions asked are on the left and the answers are on the right.

- Imagine any two different animals   *Fox*   *Snake*
- What adjective would describe each?   *sleek*   *slimy*
- What verb would you assign to each? *running*   *slithering*
- Have each animal say something to the other   *'You'll never catch me'*   *'I can kill you if I want to'*
- If the fox and the snake were in conflict, what would happen?   *The snake would bide its time, and when he had the fox in the right position, he would strike.*
- Does the conflict between the snake and the fox have anything to do with your conflict?   *I'll be damned. It sure does. It's me always waiting for the woman's approval before I will move towards her. I am angry at her for the power I give her.*

In Shorr's example, he, as therapist, asked the questions. However, there is nothing to stop you providing both the questions and answers, and by so doing, finding out more about yourself. Of course, there are many other symbols and images that you can use to help you do this.

Boxes, puzzles, crystal balls, and TV sets

Covered boxes are one. Before your closed eyes allow the image of a box to appear. There is a cover on it. As with all imagery work, do not try too hard. Just let it appear. This closed box is made of anything — wood, plastic, leather, metal; and it is of any shape — round, square, rectangular. When it is clearly established in your mind, reach out and remove the cover. Whatever you see inside can then be mentally explored in an attempt to find its meaning for you.

Sometimes people using this image find nothing. The box is empty, perhaps symbolizing a sense of inner emptiness. Should this be the case, you may like to put something in the box. On other occasions, the box may be a coffin, indicating an unresolved mourning for some loss in your life. Although the loss is usually that of a person, it could also be of an object, or of an opportunity. Often the need to go through a mourning episode is unrecognized and the coffin image is a way of drawing your attention to it. Most of the images you will get are highly individual and, with a little thought, you'll be able to work out the meaning that they carry for you.

Boxes can be used in another interesting way, too. Imagine that you are sitting at a table on which there are a number of boxes. They have no pictures on their lids, but inside each one is a complete set of pieces for a jigsaw. Choose a box, empty out the pieces and put the jigsaw together. Doing this in your imagination enables you to speed up the process tremendously. Assembling the pieces can be, say, 30 times faster than normal. This capability that we have of distorting time will be explored more fully in the next chapter, and it is certainly of great value in this jigsaw image. As you put together the pieces, a picture will form. This will normally have some meaning for you, telling you something about yourself. By going on to the other boxes, and assembling the pieces found in each of them, you will create further pictures. These may be related to the first one, or they may indicate quite separate concerns. It is almost like looking into a crystal ball.

In fact, you may like to use a crystal ball as an image to help you learn more about yourself. Just imagine yourself seated comfortably in front of a large crystal ball. Focus on it intently. Gaze into its depths. Soon you will see images appearing within. Simply let them develop so that their meaning unfolds. Or, if you prefer, you may actually suggest images relevant to some difficulty which you have, and then let them flow on without further direction.

Comparable to the use of a crystal ball is that of a television set. Imagine sitting in front of a television set. You could first see pictured there a very pleasant scene, one which enables you to induce a comfortable relaxed state. Then, allow the screen to become black. Seeing black is an excellent way of calming your mind. Permit images to form, action to take place. Do not try to deliberately control what appears on the screen. Let it happen. Are there people there? Do they remind you of anyone? As the picture changes, flow with it. Do the situations depicted tell you anything about your own situation?

You can use the image of the TV set as a safety valve for strong emotion, too. On the screen see yourself expressing your feelings towards whoever it is with whom you are concerned — wife, husband, child, parent or anyone else. If the emotion is one of anger, let it boil out, erupting like lava from a volcano. You can give free rein to repressed feelings; ventilate them, then let them go. You do not need to feel any sense of guilt, for you are using your imagination as a means of letting off steam. By doing this, you are less likely to actually inflict hurt upon the object of your anger.

As with the crystal ball, at times you might want to start with a picture that you have selected yourself, then to let the action unfold from there. Or you may want to use it as a mirror to look at your own reflection. Often, your reflected image is different from the 'real' you. Instead, it may be an idealized self, you as you would like to become. This is one of the elements in a delightful projective fantasy entitled 'Gandor's garden', which is contained in Gibbon's book, *Applied Hypnosis and Hyperempiria*.

Gandor's garden and the theatre

Imagine yourself walking down a forest path on a beautiful mild summer's day. Quite unexpectedly you come upon a large mound of freshly dug earth with a round, wooden door on one side. Your curiosity piqued, you approach the door, which is standing slightly ajar. As you look inside, you see a tunnel with dry, firm walls. Although it is very dim in the tunnel, there is a glimmer of light coming from the other end. This is quite surprising, for the tunnel actually slopes downward.

Investigating further, you enter the tunnel, following along its length as it plunges downward, ever deeper into the earth, the light at the end growing steadily brighter. Suddenly, just as you have almost reached the end, the ground gives way beneath you, and you tumble head-over-heels into a well-lit garden, coming to rest safely at the foot of a grassy knoll.

Looking upwards, you are impressed by the ingenious system of skylights which provides illumination for this underground garden. Then you are startled to hear the sound of high-pitched laughter. Turning, you see, standing almost at your elbow, a smiling elf who gestures grandly about him with his staff. 'I'm Gandor,' he says, 'and this is my garden. You are welcome. Feel free to walk around and explore, for today you are my guest.' Gandor then disappears.

You commence exploring the garden, noticing first a tiny reflecting pool nestled in the grass by the side of the knoll where you first entered. Gazing into its depths, you become aware of the very special 'magic' that this garden possesses, for there in the pool, gazing back at you, is the image of you not as you are but as you would like to become. Suddenly, this idealized image speaks, telling you something about yourself of which you had been unaware.

Give yourself time to hear this message, then continue on the pathway through the garden until you round a bend and come upon a little child, happily skipping with a rope. The child smiles, beckons to you, and as you bend down to her, she whispers in your ear, telling you something about yourself that you had almost forgotten. This message relates to your own early years, reminding you of something which needs to be remembered now to help you live more fully in the present. Listen to the secret.

As the child skips happily away, you continue to follow the path, arriving at a small clearing where three butterflies are dancing joyfully in the air. You can hear them humming a tune and, as you come closer, you can make out the words. They are singing about happiness and about what constitutes the true secret of being happy. This is of great interest to you. Stop a while, and listen to their song.

Once you have done so, you resume your walk. You have almost reached the end of the path when you notice an old man sitting cross-legged beside it. He appears to be meditating, but he opens his eyes at your approach as if he had been expecting you. The old man begins to speak, and from his lips you gain some especially wise advice on a matter with which you have been concerned.

With this advice fresh in your mind, you complete your journey, returning to the grassy knoll where Gandor awaits you. 'Now you will be going back to the outside world,' he says, 'but you will remember with great fondness everything that has happened here. You will be delighted with the great insights which will grow out of your experience obtained here in the magic garden. Naturally, you can return as often as you wish, and each time you do so, there will be more surprises and helpful insights awaiting you.' So, you take your leave of Gandor, go back up the passage, and return to the original forest, taking back with you the wisdom which you have received.

A fantasy such as this enables you to tap wisdom which is already yours but of which you are not yet consciously aware. By attaining this unconscious awareness you gain increased insight into yourself, learning more about the person you are. Many other fantasies will do this for you, too.

A popular one is the theatre image. A way of using this is to imagine yourself sitting in the stalls waiting for the performance to begin. As you wait, you notice someone standing on the side of the stage peering behind the closed curtains. This person can see what is taking place on the stage behind the curtains. *You* cannot do so. What this person sees is making him or her look very frightened and unhappy. The curtains now open so that you can see the cause of these negative reactions. Because you project your own fears and sources of unhappiness upon this imaginary person, you will become aware of them.

In the same way you can have this person looking very happy as if his or her dearest wishes have been fulfilled. Again, you can gain additional insight into yourself through using this image. Sometimes, it can be used to also solve problems. Imagine the person first looking very puzzled, and later looking very happy as he or she finds the solution to the problem.

Gandor's wise old man has been often used to serve this end, too — providing advice on how to reduce pain, provide protection, make decisions, and improve the quality of one's life generally. Obviously, being able to solve problems effectively is likely to make life more pleasant. So in the next chapter we'll look at imagery which is likely to help us in this area.

5 Solving Problems and Distorting Time

The blackboard

Blackboards are very useful images for the purpose of problem-solving. One simple technique is to suggest that you will see, written on the board, a single word which will provide a clue to the problem at hand. Use this word as a starting point for association. Write up another word suggested by the first one, then another suggested by the second one, and so on. This process will often provide clarification for you.

You may prefer to visualize a blackboard while suggesting to yourself that 'something' will be written on it pertinent to the problem which you have in mind. This 'something' could be much more than the single word of the first technique. Alternatively, you may prefer to write your problem on one side of the blackboard, turn it over, and then write the solution which you may not have realized you knew until you started writing.

John Eldridge, a businessman, uses the board technique as a means of clarifying his goals. He imagines the board, chalk tray, chalk, and an eraser. Taking up a piece of chalk, he prints 'my current goals' in the centre of the board; then he draws a rectangle around those words. Towards the upper right-hand corner of the board, he prints 'Goals I eagerly pursue', and towards the upper left-hand corner, 'Goals I half-heartedly pursue'. Circles are placed around these words, as they are around 'Goals I don't know I have', in the lower left-hand part of the

56

board, and 'Goals I take no action towards', in the lower right-hand corner.

John then writes down on the board everything that is going on in his life that could be called a goal. If it is obvious which of the four headings the goal falls under, he writes it in the appropriate part of the board, but otherwise he puts it anywhere. Not just practical, down-to-earth, everyday goals appear on John's blackboard. He gives his imagination full rein, thinking not only of his present needs, but also of the future, asking himself 'How would I like to live five years from now? What personal qualities would I like to have? What material possession would I desire?'

Once he has written down everything he can think of, John classifies his goals, using arrows to link them to their appropriate heading. Then he looks long and hard at those grouped under 'Goals I half-heartedly pursue'. 'Do I really want these things?' he asks himself. He also asks this of the other goals scattered all over the board, particularly those where it appears that they are not of his own choosing. 'Does it,' he asks himself, 'give me any satisfaction to think of those goals as accomplished?'

John then imagines that he leaves his blackboard for a few seconds, turning away from it. When he turns back again to face it, the board has changed. The goals that really excite him now glow brightly. Not all of these are in the upper right-hand corner, though most are. Some appear in the lower left, as goals that John did not even know he had; and, occasionally, one of the previously half-heartedly pursued goals also glow brightly. All of these are then connected by arrows to the 'Goals I eagerly pursue' heading.

Actually John learnt of this goal-clarification use of the blackboard from *Hypnosis with Friends and Lovers*, a book written by Freda Morris. She suggests that once important goals have been identified in this way, you should state them:

- *Positively* — not 'I stop smoking' but 'Every breath I take fills my lungs with the cleanest pure air available'
- *In the present tense*, as if the goals were already reached
- *In the active voice* — 'I have reduced my weight by 10 kilos'; for this reminds you that you have to *do* something.

On your list, which really needs to be written down, perhaps on special paper because of its importance to you, set an order of priority. Imagine achieving these high-priority goals as you fall asleep at night. When you wake in the morning, concentrate on them again and imagine yourself doing something towards their achievement this day.

Impressed by the change which she saw in John, mainly attributed to his imaginative use of blackboard techniques, Paula, his wife, has found a use for this approach too. She visualizes herself entering a very pleasant room, one wall of which is made of glass, looking out onto a beautiful garden, and another wall of which contains a large blackboard. Paula imagines herself going to the blackboard, picking up a piece of chalk and drawing a line which divides the board into two halves. On the left-hand side of the board she writes a word such as 'misery'. This word is written quite small and is then wiped out with a blackboard duster. Paula then goes to the right-hand side of the board and writes, in much larger letters, 'happiness'. This word remains on the board while she looks at it in her imagination.

Paula then returns to the left-hand side of the board to write another word such as 'depression', again quite small. She immediately wipes out this word, going back to the right-hand side of the board and writing in large letters the word 'joy'. This word remains; and so the process is repeated, with words summarizing negative states being written on the left-hand side of the board and wiped off, while words summarizing positive states are written larger on the right-hand side of the board and allowed to remain there. At the end of this little exercise Paula looks at the board, thinks about what the words remaining there mean, then goes to the other side of the room to look out through the windows at the beautiful garden, as she experiences a feeling of joy and happiness within herself.

This method is for many people an effective way of changing their moods, a topic which will be pursued in Chapter 11. Certainly, Paula finds that it usually enables her to shrug off unwanted feelings. She uses it together with other images which help her handle problems. Paula's favourite image has her looking at a sky full of clouds, knowing that a slight breeze is coming which will blow all these away. Once the clouds have gone, a scene that was previously hidden is clearly revealed, and this clarifies some particular problem about which she is concerned.

The affect bridge

Many of the problems about which we are concerned have their roots in the past, and there are some interesting ways of using the imagination to overcome such difficulties. One is the affect bridge, a means of going from the present to a past traumatic situation which is not known consciously. The idea is to look into the present inappropriate feeling and follow it back to its source.

To illustrate, let's look at how Ron Aldridge, a man given to violent temper outbursts, used the procedure to make life more pleasant both for himself and for those around him. Firstly, while sitting quietly, Ron relaxed, letting both body and mind become relatively still. He then activated the unpleasant feeling, his violent anger and temper, by recalling a recent situation when he behaved in this way. This he mentally recreated as vividly as possible, intensifying the feeling to recapture as much of the original force as he could.

Next, Ron let the actual circumstances, the situation itself, fade away while he focused exclusively upon the feeling of becoming increasingly angry. This feeling he followed back in time, as if it was a long rope or bridge leading to the first occasion when he had felt this anger. Ron visualized this situation, finding out how old he was, what was happening, and making certain that it was really the first time that he ever experienced the violent feeling. Actually, he did not get back to the first experience initially, but he continued to follow the feeling further into the past until he was quite sure that he had successfully identified and recreated imaginatively the first of his temper outbursts.

Then Ron reversed the process. He came back up the rope, forward to the next time that he had had a violent temper outburst. This he re-experienced, as he did with each succeeding one. However, as well as reliving each situation in his imagination, he re-evaluated it from an adult viewpoint. While he understood why the child he was had acted in this way, he realized that, as an adult, he no longer needed to engage in such behaviour.

This same technique may be applied to eliminate a sense of the negative. In this case, recall some incident or incidents from the recent past where you feel dissatisfied with yourself. Perhaps you were ashamed of your incompetence, angry at yourself for being too timid, or guilty about overreacting to a trivial annoyance. The actual situation does not matter. What is important is the feeling that accompanies a sense of dissatisfaction with yourself. Intensify this feeling. Really wallow in the sensation of having done something wrong, of having been a failure.

Follow this feeling of failure back in time, to those occasions when you felt it before. Do not try to force your memory. Let it happen — and it will. These occasions will come into your mind. In your imagination, relive each one, every time increasing that feeling of failure, of worthlessness. Usually you will go back to the first occasion on which this dull emptiness, this displeasure with yourself, was present.

Now, breathe deeply. Let go more completely, allowing the negative emotions to fade away while still retaining this first incident. Remake this situation. Change it so that you become a winner. Work back to the present, changing each failure into a success, experiencing the positive feelings instead of the negative ones. From your present adult viewpoint, you can clean up these childhood failures, knowing you now have resources to handle such situations far more effectively, just as you can cope more positively with your present negative situation.

Back to the theatre

Sometimes it is desirable to distance yourself when you are reworking these past memories so that they lose their negative influence. Use of the theatre image, described in the last chapter, is one way of doing so. You see a scene from your own past, perhaps dating back to a time several minutes before you first experienced your particular bad habit, negative emotional state, or type of behaviour that you wish to change. Wait. Let the scene appear by itself on the empty stage in front of you. Simply imagine yourself sitting calm and relaxed in a comfortable, soft seat as the situation develops before you.

Once your scene appears, you can view it dispassionately, as if you are looking in from outside. Without experiencing tension, anxiety, or pain, detect the moment when the character on the stage who is playing 'you' first began to feel discomfort. What was happening to cause that response? Ensure that you remain relaxed, looking at the event 'out there' on the stage. If you find yourself becoming agitated or tense, turn off the image for a moment and concentrate on your breathing, letting go with each out-breath. This ability to switch images on and off is of great value in using your imagination to help yourself. Once you relax again, go back to the theatre.

As the scene nears its conclusion, consider how the onstage 'you' feels. What has he or she done or not done to contribute to the undesired result? Then let the scene fade away. Now you are going to rewrite the script. Replay the scene out there on the stage as you would like it to be. Imagine yourself saying and doing the things that would change that past failure into a success. To a large extent our habits and physical symptoms can be seen as a script which our bodies automatically follow whenever we are in certain types of situation. By changing that script through the use of imagination, you can create new habits and physical symptoms which are positive rather than negative.

If, for example, you trace a certain painful feeling back to a time early in your life when your mother sent you angrily away as you approached her, change the image. Replace the rejection with a positive image created around the same theme. Visualize the child that was you approaching your mother who accepts you warmly, cuddling you in her arms. Remake your past history and you can change your present quite dramatically. This entails being able to re-experience your past through a process of age regression.

Age regression

The techniques described in this chapter involve your going back to a time when you were younger so that you can relive past events. Some of us are able to do this very vividly. We really *do* relive such experiences. Others are able to remember satisfactorily, but do not have the same sense of going back in time. Despite this, such people are still able to achieve excellent results through the age-regression approaches to be described. Once again, more success is likely to be experienced if you first allow yourself to drift into a trance state, using your imagination in a relaxed, unforced way.

See before you the book of time, a book in which you will find photographs from your entire life. The page now open reveals a photograph of you as you now are, because this is your present age. Turn the page back one year, and suddenly you can be there again, feeling what you felt then, knowing what you knew then. You can continue turning the pages, one at a time, going back fully and completely each year, being able to stop at any stage to explore experiences which you may have had at that age. Then, when you want to return to your present age, you turn the pages of the book of time forward. Thus you can, with ease, move back and forth in your past.

Or perhaps you might like to go into a special room, its walls lined with bookshelves. These hold diaries, one for each year of your life. You may wish to use these diaries to find information relevant to your present problem or to simply learn more about your past life. As well as using the diaries to do this, you might also like to make use of old photographs, report cards, and letters which are stored in drawers beneath the bookshelves.

Attics or storerooms are interesting places in which to recapture aspects of our past lives. They are full of discarded junk, toys, memorabilia of all descriptions. You can pick up an object and return to the age you were when you used it. One way of helping yourself to do so is to imagine the object becoming larger as you grow smaller. You see a door in the object through which you can enter. As you step through, you become the age at which it appeared in your life. You can re-experience events in your life at that age, then return to your present size by coming back through the door.

There are many other ways of using your imagination to enable you to go back in time. Visualize yourself getting on a train. This is a very special vehicle, a time train. As you gaze out the window you find yourself being transported back through various periods of your life. The milestones that you pass are the milestones of your life, the scenes that you see from the window are the events that have happened to you. When a particularly important event is reached, the train will stop, and you can get off to explore the situation more fully. When you are ready, the train will transport you back to the present.

Using a calendar can also be an effective stimulus for age regression. Imagine the calendar set at today's date. As fast as you like, you can flip back through the dates which will span your entire life, stopping at any point which seems of particular interest. Return by reversing the procedure.

You might even like to take a magic carpet ride, floating in the air over a broad 'river of time'. Downstream is the future, upstream is the past. Immediately below you is a milestone representing the present year. Your carpet flies upstream, floating over milestone after milestone until it stops at a time important to you.

All these techniques are flexible and easy to use. They can also be enjoyed as we appreciate the power of our imagination to take us through time and space effortlessly so that we can meet ourselves as we were when younger. It is often very helpful to become re-acquainted with the child in ourselves, repossessing, loving, and cherishing.

An interesting way of doing this quite explicitly is to imagine that the child you were is standing at the door to the room in which you are sitting. What would that child look like? How old is the child? What is the child wearing? How does the child feel about coming into the room to meet you? How would you, as your present adult self with your present adult knowledge and insight, deal with this kind of child were he or she to enter the room now? How would you help the child to feel wanted, valuable, loved? Possibly, there are many other questions that you could ask yourself as you imaginatively interacted with the child that was you.

Turning back time in the ways which I have described enables you to learn a lot about yourself and the source of your present problems. Of course, there is nothing particularly unusual about this idea of age regression. We do it quite naturally and quite frequently without deliberately setting out to do so. Distorting time is, in other words, an everyday occurrence.

Distortion of time

Time is not really what it appears to be. Sometimes it can go very quickly. Think of times when you were really enjoying yourself. How time flew. Recall when you may have been completely engrossed in a conversation, a book, or a film, and compare that with other occasions when you were bored. Though the clock time involved may have been the same, in the first case time passed quickly and in the second case, slowly. I can still remember how the boring, dull, academic university lectures seemed to last forever whilst the lively ones seemed to end so quickly. Yet, the clock time in both cases was 50 minutes.

We do not move through time at a constant rate. It varies. We vary. We can use this phenomenon to our advantage. Beryl Sharp, an ex-patient of mine, is one person who has done so. Beryl disliked flying. Though I was able to reduce her terror of being in a plane to a more moderate dislike, she still preferred not to fly. Unfortunately, in her work as a sales representative she was required to make several inter-state trips a year, some of them over quite long distances. The answer, for Beryl, was time distortion. From the time when she stepped into the plane, one hour of clock time became equivalent to five minutes. She speeded up time so that a four-hour flight seemed then to take only 20 minutes.

Though this may sound impossible, it is really not all that difficult to achieve. If we can accept that, in our normal day-to-day life, time sometimes passes quickly and sometimes slowly, this means that we have within us the resources to deliberately manipulate time to suit our own purposes.

Children do this quite easily. One of the induction techniques which I use with children is to ask them to see their favourite television programme. All I do is tell them that they will have, say, three minutes to do so, but that the programme will seem to flash by very quickly, giving them plenty of time to view it from start to end. Children appear to have little difficulty in distinguishing their own subjective time from clock time. They know that time moves slowly when they are anxiously waiting for Christmas to arrive. Also, they know that it moves quickly when they have a dental appointment next week.

One way of practising time distortion for yourself is to use the image of an old grandfather clock. On this special clock, you can move the hands slower or faster to arrive at a particular time, and also at a particular date, which is shown on a panel below the clockface. Thus, you can use your imagination to experience an event occurring more quickly or more slowly than it did in actuality.

Beryl Sharp, for example, was able to return to that time, three years previous, when her father had died. As she had been unable to express any real grief, she had felt guilty ever since. In a clock-time period of five minutes, she experienced three days of mourning. On another occasion, when she was called upon to give evidence as a witness to a car accident, she regressed to the time of the incident, re-experiencing in a one-minute period of slow motion that which had actually occupied ten minutes of clock time.

Beryl does not possess magical powers. She has simply learned to make use of a resource which we all have. Using her imagination helps her do so. It helps her handle problems, too; for, just as she uses age regression to go back in time, so she uses age progression to go forward in time. If she has a problem, she imagines herself three months in the future. At this time, the problem has been solved. She then asks herself: 'How did I solve this?' Her unconscious mind then provides her with the steps that she took. These she can then apply in the present.

This approach, together with many other of the techniques which are outlined in this chapter, is quite applicable to handling anxiety states, a subject which we consider next.

6 Handling Anxiety Through Your Imagination

Of colours, fists, screens, and compartments.

Let's begin with some examples. Whenever she was called upon to entertain her in-laws, Julie Harrington became very anxious. She felt herself to be 'under test' on such occasions, experiencing the same sort of anxiety that students feel when sitting for examinations. To help her overcome this problem I asked Julie to imagine the dinner party as it usually took place and to concentrate on describing her anxious feelings. After some thought, she said that she felt 'all puffed out', as if she had a balloon inside her. I asked Julie to describe this balloon in some detail, giving its shape, size, colour, and texture. When she had done so, I suggested that she change one or more of these aspects, noting what happened to the anxiety feeling. Colour was the feature which worked best for her. When she changed the green balloon to yellow, she felt her tension ease quite markedly. Other colours did not achieve the same effect, nor did varying the shape, size or texture of the balloon.

Stuart Roberts' anxiety surfaces when he has to give instructions to employees at the store where he works as a department manager. He is able to control the feeling reasonably well by taking a few deep breaths, imagining that all his tension is flowing into his right fist, and clenching it gradually as he imagines this happening. Finally, his fist is tightened as much as possible. All anxiety is locked up in it. Once he feels there is no noticeable tension left anywhere else in his body, he opens his fist and lets it go. This instant release usually works better for Stuart than gradual relaxation to a count of 10 slow, deep breaths. However, others may find this latter method more effective.

Marlene Hindley uses a 'worry screen' to help her cope with anxiety. She visualizes a movie screen. This is somewhere 'out there', separate from her. When things happen which arouse tension and anxiety, she puts them out on her 'worry screen' instead of inflicting them on her mind and body. As they are no longer part of her, Marlene can let her worries do whatever they want to do, but she does not have to be concerned about them. Should she wish to, she can deal with them later. Alternatively, she may prefer to let them go completely.

Jim Danielson does something similar. A factory foreman, he uses compartmentalization to handle his anxieties. This involves putting troubles and problems away in compartments when there is no longer any point in worrying or thinking about them. Much of our own unhappiness is caused by vague, diffuse worries and fears which race round like squirrels in our minds, preventing us from thinking clearly. If we make our problems concrete, perhaps by writing them down, they are much easier to handle. We will often see that our worrying avails us nothing. We have a choice: should we continue to worry about them, allowing them to disturb us, or should we simply put them out of our minds? This is often difficult to do and the concept of compartmentalizing can be helpful.

At one point in James Clavell's great book *Shogun*, the Japanese lady, Mariko, is talking to the Englishman, Blackthorne, when he has been upset through arguing with the Catholic priest. Mariko says: 'Please, I implore you to be Japanese. Put this incident away, that's all it is, one incident in ten thousand. You must not allow it to wreck your harmony. Put it away into a compartment, put all things into their own separate compartments.'

Visualization can help this process. Imagine a huge house or castle comprising many rooms. Visualize yourself entering the castle, going to a particular room, opening the door and placing a problem inside. Then you leave, shutting the door behind you, resolving not to bring that particular problem or worry out again until you can do something constructive about it.

Julie, Stuart, Marlene, and Jim all use their imagination to help them handle anxiety more effectively. Though we may have difficulty in actually defining this state, we certainly know when we feel anxious. Our minds are troubled and we feel uneasy, often as if something terrible — we know not what — is going to happen. There may be physical symptoms, such as sweating palms, upset stomach and headaches, as well as psychological symptoms of irritability and impatience. Our bodies and minds are aroused by the extra adrenalin flowing into our system. We are ready to fight or flee. Unfortunately, we usually either do not know whom or what we have to fight or flee from; or, if we do know, we cannot actually engage in this physical activity. We have to suppress the fight or flight response. So we need to find other ways of reducing our state of heightened arousal. Let us look at some more ways of doing so, again making use of our most powerful weapon — our imagination.

Detachment

The approach adopted by both Marlene and Jim involves the concept of detachment, of separation from the source of anxiety, or, should that source be unknown, from the actual symptoms produced. We tend to be dominated by everything with which we become identified. Conversely, we can take control over everything from which we can dis-identify ourselves. For example, every time we identify ourselves with sickness, fear, or failure, every time we admit 'I am angry' or 'I am irritated', we become increasingly dominated by sickness, fear, failure, anger, or irritability. We claim these things as our own by identifying ourselves with them. But we do not have to. We could put it differently: 'A feeling of failure is trying to submerge me', or 'A wave of irritability is attempting to overpower me'. What is happening here is that we separate ourselves from the feelings of failure and irritability, refusing to own them as part of us.

The distinction may seem slight. It isn't. It is very important. You have a body — but you are not your body. After all, within a few days, the cells of your body will no longer be the same. You use a body, just as you use a car, but you are the driver, the controlling force. Similarly, you have emotions such as love, hate, elation, depression; but you are not these emotions. They are all passing moods. Neither are you your thoughts. True, you think; but during any one day, thousands of thoughts pass through your mind. You are not those thoughts. You can separate yourself from them as if they were birds floating through your mind, choosing to retain only those that you wish to keep and allowing the others to disappear.

Once you realize that you do possess considerable power to detach yourself from your body, your emotions and your thoughts, you can greatly reduce the control which you have permitted anxiety to exert over your life. To counteract extreme nervousness, for example, you may care to practice the following procedure.

Sit or lie comfortably with your eyes closed, paying attention passively to anything which goes on in your body. Do not analyze or intellectualize. Simply pay attention as you scan your body and report out loud whatever is happening. This might be something like: 'Pressure in the chest; eyelids fluttering; itch on right ear; discomfort in right foot.' Omit all unnecessary words and any reference to yourself. It is 'discomfort in the right foot', and not 'My right foot feels uncomfortable'.

By observing dispassionately and verbalizing the results of your observations, you will gradually diminish your restlessness in body and mind. After a few minutes, the sensations become fewer, followed by increasing calmness — and, perhaps, sleep. Once you train yourself in such detachment, you can often achieve separation from high arousal states without having to sit down and close your eyes. Another way of handling such states is through a mental scale.

The 'comfort' scale

Jennifer Turnley spends a lot of time at home by herself. Her children have grown up and left home, her husband travels a lot, and she has relatively few friends. At times, she used to be subject to such acute anxiety feelings that she would vomit. This pattern of behaviour existed for several years before she found a way of controlling her high arousal state. Once I had shown her what to do, Jennifer was able to follow the procedure for herself without any further assistance, though she did require considerable practice before she achieved the level of control she desired.

I asked Jennifer to imagine vividly the situation which had existed a few moments before her last vomiting attack. In that situation she described what was happening and how she was feeling; and, on a 10-point anxiety scale (0 = the calmest she had ever been, 10 = the most anxious she had ever been), she placed herself at 9. Jennifer was then asked to say to herself the word 'calm' and, as she did so, to imagine herself becoming increasingly relaxed, coming down the scale to a level at which she felt comfortable. This she practised several times. Her best results were achieved when she synchronized her 'calm' with an out-breath, coming down one point on the scale each time that she breathed out.

Jennifer was most comfortable when she reached point 4 on the scale. She was able, on occasions, to get down to 1, but she felt sluggish and lethargic when she did so. She would then reverse the procedure, saying 'alert' to herself each time that she drew in a breath, going up one point on the scale for each breath. In this way she assumed an increased level of control over her arousal state. Whenever she felt overaroused, and before she reached the vomiting stage, Jennifer would visualize her scale, realize at what level she was, and reduce it to her comfort level, point 4. Sometimes she would have to do this several times before she could stabilize at her desired level. Other people using this 'comfort' scale approach do find, as did Jennifer, that persistence is necessary, particularly in situations which involve conflict.

Coping with conflict situations

Conflict is often an important factor in the creation of anxiety. Whatever the cause of the indecision, you can use your imagination to cope with it more effectively. In fact, you might care to combine a conflict-resolving stimulus to the unconscious mind with a pleasant trance induction.

One way of doing this is to imagine yourself in a state of indecision. A part of you says 'I want to do it', while another part says 'I don't want to do it'. Imagine that each of your hands is one side of this conflict. Raise them now, well apart. Look at them. Though they are apart, you want them to come together so that you will be complete, as a unity — with no more conflict, no more indecision between needs, no more apartness. As you continue to focus on your hands, let them move closer and closer, as if drawn together by some magnetic force. You may need to start them moving deliberately, but then let it happen by itself as you imagine the force drawing them together. As this occurs, you feel an ever-increasing sense of completeness and of unity. When your hands finally touch, and let this happen in its own time without you consciously pushing them together, you will feel a sense of harmony and contentment. Your hands can drop into your lap, your eyes may want to close, and you are at peace. Actually, as you concentrate on your hands moving ever closer, you will probably find your eyes growing heavier and heavier so that it may be a struggle to keep them open. If this happens, let them close. Continue visualizing your hands mentally until they touch and drop into your lap.

Often, concentration on one hand instead of two is easier to achieve, together with an action-induction method which involves the rising arm being linked to a lifting of conflicts and other negative states. Look at your hand as it lays on your thigh. Think about it becoming lighter. Imagine your hand wanting to lift. See it beginning to do so. As it does, your problems lift too, becoming lighter and lighter. Again, as your hand lifts, your eyes may become increasingly heavy and close. Whether they do or not, just focus on the lifting of both your arms and the negative states which you want to get rid of. Feel all conflicts vanishing so that by the time your hand touches your face, you experience great contentment and happiness. Your hand can drop into your lap as you enjoy this conflict-free state.

Should you have difficulty achieving such arm movement, imagine a model — for instance, someone you admire — doing it. Watch him or her, in your imagination, achieving the arm lift. At a certain point, take over yourself to complete the 'letting go' of conflict.

If you do not feel comfortable with this lifting or lightness idea, go the other way. Become aware of the natural weight of your body on the chair (or floor, or bed). Surrender your weight to the chair, allowing yourself to be supported by it. Imagine your chair being supported by the building you are in, which in turn is supported by the Earth. Allow yourself to be supported by Planet Earth. As you become grounded, settled, and at home, you can let all troubles, conflicts, and worries disappear. This is a very simple technique and there are many others, just as uncomplicated, which you can use to handle anxiety more effectively.

Anxiety-removing images

Peace images work well. I have mentioned still water, tranquility rooms, and soft, velvet blackness. Any image that you interpret to mean calm, quietness, and stillness will help you. You can increase its calming effect by taking the peace image from your mind to your body centre, which is located just below your navel. As you breathe in, see the image in your mind; as you breath out, take it to your centre. In the same way, you can transform anxiety into energy. Take it down from your mind and breathe it into your centre, where you can imagine it being transformed into energy.

You exert control over your anxiety by transforming it in this way, changing it from something negative into something positive. Other imagery can provide this experience of self-control and direction, particularly that which is related to aspects of everyday life. For example, you might like to imagine your system as similar to that of a car. By using either the accelerator or the brake you can choose to speed up or to slow down. When under pressure, imagine yourself pressing your brake pedal to reduce speed, as if in response to a big, red, stop sign. On those occasions when you do feel highly anxious, it is helpful to see this stop sign in your mind. It interrupts the flow of those anxiety-creating statements which you are probably telling yourself and it serves as a reminder that you have the ability to slow down, to reduce the pressure of destructive emotions.

These destructive, negative emotions may also be wrapped up as variously sized parcels, and packed into a huge, empty suitcase. To get the suitcase shut, you may have to sit on the lid. Once you get it shut, it is locked away in a cupboard. A little later, you can get it out, open it, and find that the enormous bulging case has shrunk to the size of a small bag. Or you may simply prefer to leave the case locked in the cupboard and throw away the key.

You might also want, in imagination, to go to your

stomach, feel around in there, and find out what is going on. Are there butterflies, knots, worry, tension, anxiety, and other nameless things which you do not want there? Imagine yourself taking them out, wrapping them in one huge ball which you have in your hands, and throwing it away, feeling a sense of great release as you do so.

The same sense of release can be experienced by visualizing a pressure cooker. See the steam being released. The more steam you let out, the more mental relief you can feel. It is useful for you to have some way of letting off steam when you are anxious under pressure. If it is impossible to do this physically, your imagination can provide an alternative.

Yet another way of coping is to imagine the worst thing that could happen if you were confronted by the anxiety-provoking situation. Visualize this as vividly as you can. Then see yourself coping in a competent, relaxed manner, improving upon the situation, and producing a favourable outcome. This is an approach that people sometimes use to overcome phobias, though there are, perhaps, more effective ways of doing so.

Overcoming phobias

Phobias are persistent and irrational fears of a specific object, activity or situation resulting in a compelling desire to avoid this dreaded object, activity, or situation. Probably the most common phobias are fear of heights, closed-in spaces, open spaces, competitive situations (such as examinations), animals (especially snakes and spiders), dentists, doctors, and blood. Such fears may range from being mildly annoying to being so severely incapacitating that they interfere with a person's life, preventing that person from doing the things he or she would like to do.

Wayne Brown hates flying. Although he knows all about the safety statistics and realizes that he runs more risks of being killed in his car or on a bus than on a plane, he is still so terrified that he will go to incredible lengths to avoid flying. Since his divorce several years ago, Wayne has moved to a different State. But he returns frequently to see his three children who live with his ex-wife. He will choose to spend days travelling by road rather than face several hours in an aeroplane.

The same pattern can be seen in his avoidance of elevators. Wayne will tramp up unnumerable flights of stairs, and then tramp down again, because he is too frightened to use an elevator. He is not alone in this. Many people share Wayne's phobias, just as they share that of the eleven-year-old Nancy Bateman.

Nancy is terrified of injections. Whether these are administered by a dentist, doctor, or nurse is immaterial. Even the thought of having an injection causes extreme panic. Unfortunately, Nancy has leukaemia. Her treatment involves quite painful injections of bone marrow at regular intervals. For the week before each treatment, Nancy is physically ill, sobbing much of the time and living in abject fear.

So is Tom Bradley, though his phobia is of a different source. He is petrified of examinations. No matter how well he knows his work, he 'freezes' once he enters the examination room. For weeks before, he stews, knowing this is going to happen, but he cannot do anything about it.

Fortunately there are measures that we can take to overcome phobias. Again, our imagination is a great ally.

One use of it is through a procedure termed 'systematic desensitization'. This involves setting up a careful sequence of activities to be pictured in your mind, ranging from the least frightening aspects to the most frightening. It is helpful to write down these steps, somewhat along the lines which are described by Singer and Switzer. For instance, if you have a phobia about driving a car, you might use a sequence such as the one suggested by these writers. After using a suitable induction, you could:

- *Step 1*   Imagine you are looking over your car, checking that it is roadworthy and without dangerous defects. With you is someone knowledgeable about road safety whom you like and trust
- *Step 2*   Imagine that this person is driving you around the neighbourhood, giving you useful pointers on road safety
- *Step 3*   Picture yourself, still as a passenger, with this same person driving at top legal speed on a freeway
- *Step 4*   Visualize yourself taking the wheel of a car with the same person beside you as a passenger
- *Step 5*   Imagine yourself driving alone, slowly and carefully in a well-known neighbourhood
- *Step 6*   Picture yourself driving confidently and quickly on a freeway.

Extra steps may be added, so as to make the transition from the least to the most frightening aspects more gradual. If, at any time, while imagining yourself performing these steps you start to feel anxious, switch away to think of something relaxing. This is where it is useful to have a 'special place' of tranquility in your mind. Once you calm down, you can then return to the step at which you had trouble. Continue switching back and forth until you can imagine performing the activity in a relaxed, comfortable way. Then you can move on to the next step. Once you can imagine yourself driving at ease on the freeway around your neighbourhood, you will probably be able to do so in practice.

If this gradual, step-by-step visualization approach does not appeal to you, you might like another clenched-fist piece of imagery. Recall the happiest day of your life: how it started, what happened, and all the associations that it has for you. As you do this, clench your right hand if right-handed or left hand if left-handed. This dominant hand represents all that is good, strong, and normal. It is the better-trained hand and has had the most meaning since birth. Switch from your happiest day to other very happy memories, clenching the dominant hand again. Then, relax.

Now visualize a situation in which your phobia is operating. Experience the feelings associated with it as vividly as possible — the fear, trembling, nausea, or whatever. Clench your non-dominant hand as you do. As long as your fist is locked, you will continue to have the phobia symptoms. Then, unclench the fist once you have let the tension build up. As you do so, you will feel a sense of enormous relief. Now, clench your dominant hand again. You will get an equally strong feeling of confidence, determination, and self-control. In future, when experiencing the phobic symptoms, clench the non-dominant hand to intensify these feelings, then unclench your fist to enjoy the relief, and clench the dominant hand and feel happy. Once the happiness is established, unclench the dominant hand.

Mental 'switching'

This fist routine is a way of strengthening the mental 'switching' which lies at the heart of most techniques of overcoming phobias. Wayne Brown, whom I referred to earlier for his fear of flying and of elevators, uses a 'switching' technique to cope more effectively. For example, he concentrates on the sensations in his feet while on the way to a certain address which will involve the use of an elevator. As he waits, Wayne is acutely aware of every sensation in his feet — the feel of his socks, the pressure exerted by his shoes, the tingling in his toes, and anything else which he can experience. So preoccupied does his mind become that he is distracted from the actual behaviour of entering the elevator and travelling in it. Once he leaves the lift, he 'switches' his mind away from his feet and to the business he has in hand. Peculiar as this might sound, it works for Wayne.

As far as his flying phobia is concerned, Wayne handles this by mental rehearsal. For a week or so before he is due to fly, he spends 15 to 20 minutes a day inducing a trance and imagining his journey from the time that he leaves home to the time that he arrives safely at his destination. If, at any time, his relaxed trance state is disturbed by anxiety, he mentally 'switches' his thoughts to something pleasant.

He uses the 'jewel box' technique at such times. In his head, Wayne imagines that he has a 'jewel box' containing every positive thing that has ever happened to him. Whenever he feels bad, or whenever the fear of flying surfaces, he dips into this 'jewel box', takes out a pleasant memory and thinks about it. When the anxiety subsides, he returns to his mental rehearsal of the flight, emphasizing the sense of comfort and enjoyment which he will experience. He triggers off these positive feelings by the use of a special cue. As he 'clicks' his seat belt into place, the sound is a signal for Wayne to relax deeply. By rehearsing this successful flight, Wayne is preparing his mind for success instead of fear-engendered failure.

Tom Bradley uses similar mental rehearsal to overcome his examination phobia. Through imagining the whole examination procedure in terms of success, Tom has been able to transform a very stressful situation into a challenge which he welcomes. He visualizes entering the room, sitting at his table, turning over the examination paper, finding the ideas for answering flowing easily into his mind, starting on the easiest question and then getting more ideas for other questions as he does so. This means that each new question becomes easier than the one before as ideas combine and recombine almost by themselves. Tom even sees himself receiving the mark that he wants.

Nancy Bateman has learnt to overcome her phobia too. Mental 'switching' is involved here as well. Initially, Nancy achieved some success by focusing her attention on her breathing, thinking 'one' as she inhaled, and then taking that 'one' down to her body centre below her navel. She would do sets of numbers, going up to 10. However, this technique did not work as well as she wanted until the numbers were changed into dolls of different colours. Then she could 'switch' away from the fear of the injection to concentrate on these dolls being breathed into her mind and dropping by parachute into her centre.

When you allow your mind to dwell on your fears, you increase your phobic symptoms. 'Switching' your mind away to concentrate on something else reduces them. If you can use humour, all the better. An ex-patient of mine who was once an agrophobic (she was afraid to move out of her house because of her fear of open places) has overcome her fears by the use of her sense of the ridiculous. She has a marvellous stock of peculiar images. For example, should she feel a panic attack coming on while she is shopping, she goes to a frozen food counter. There she imagines herself as a fish lying down and hiding among all the other frozen goods. What works, works! This lady has actually learnt to play with her fears by image-changing. The more ridiculous the image, the better it is for her.

So, basically, handling anxiety and fear more effectively is a matter of interrupting these negative states by 'switching' away to a contrary state. This contrary state usually has something to do with relaxation, because the relaxed state is incompatible with anxiety. In the next chapter we look at some simple ways of becoming more relaxed.

7 Imaginative Relaxation

Relaxing physically

The relaxation that we need to combat anxiety and other negative emotional states may be purely physical. Imagination can help a lot in creating this state. An approach adopted by many people would go something like this:

After getting into a comfortable sitting position, transfer your awareness from the outside world to the inside of your body. To do this, close your eyes and follow your breath as it flows in and out. As your source of life energy, your breath is the connection between your inner and outer worlds. You can strengthen your concentration by imagining your breath as a vapour, being drawn into your mouth, down your windpipe, into your lungs, stomach, solar plexus, and then out again into the world. Just let your breathing flow, unforced and spontaneous. Should your mind wander, gently bring it back to your breath.

Now, shift your focus. Become sensitive to your body. Place your awareness in each part, beginning at your head. How does it feel to be in the top of your head? Is there any tension or discomfort there? If so, breathe into the area, cleansing and bathing it with energy. As you exhale, imagine all tension or discomfort flowing out of that part of your body.

Let your consciousness descend to your face. Be aware of how it feels, noting any discomfort of tension. Remove this by bathing it with your breath and exhaling the tension as you let your breath go. Enjoy the relaxation of your face.

Continue to work down your body, neck, shoulders, arms, hands, chest, stomach, waist, genitals, hips, legs, and feet. Use the same pattern of focusing your attention on each part: bathe and soothe it with your breath, exhale the tension, and enjoy the relaxed feeling which results.

Take some time to experience the pleasure of your relaxed body and the feeling of calmness which will also be present. Continue to follow your breath in and out, so that with each exhalation you may be able to let go even more. Then allow yourself to slowly drift back to reality.

After you have completed your relaxation session, carry the good feelings with you as you go about your daily tasks. Should you find yourself under pressure and feeling stressed, recall the state of relaxation which you experienced and recreate it in your body through imagining yourself doing it again.

Another way of achieving physical relaxation quickly is to lie down on the floor, becoming acutely conscious of your body touching the surface at all points — head, shoulder, buttocks, thighs, heels. Feel the heaviness of your body pulling you down and down into the floor which supports you. The more you allow it to do so and the heavier you feel, the more you will seem to be sinking down. You can imagine the floor as a cloud, a bed of leaves, or anything else that you wish. When you have enjoyed your deep relaxation, reverse the process by feeling a sense of increased lightness as you float back to the surface.

A systematic way of creating a sense of deep physical relaxation is through autogenic training. This method, described by Luthe in *Autogenic Therapy* involves learning and practising six standard formulas. These are:

- *Heaviness.* 'My right arm is comfortably heavy'. When, through this verbal suggestion and the use

of imagination, the right arm does feel heavy, the
formula is extended to include the other limbs:
'My left arm ..., both arms ..., my right leg ...,
my left leg ..., both legs ..., arms and legs   are
comfortably heavy'.

- *Warmth.*   'My right arm is comfortably warm':
the same progressive procedure as with heaviness
is used with the warmth formula so it is extended
to all limbs.
- *Heartbeat.*   'My heartbeat is calm and regular'.
- *Respiration.* 'My respiration is regular — it breathes
me'.
- *Internal warmth.* 'My solar plexus is comfortably warm'.
- *Coolness of the forehead.* 'My forehead is comfortably cool'.

Luthe suggests that these exercises should be practised
three times daily. Doing so with the eyes shut is
recommended as an aid to concentration. During each
practice session, the sequence of formulas and the
procedure for ending the exercise ('Flex and stretch arms!
Inhale or yawn deeply! Open eyes!') is repeated three
times. Each formula should be repeated four to seven
times within each practice session, the formula for
heaviness being practised for at least one week before the
other five formulas are added, each one at approximately
a week's intervals. Thus the training periods become
progressively longer.

Luthe believes that a minimum of six weeks is
necessary for learning the six standard exercises. As
training progresses and as all six formulas have been
added successively and learned, he feels that the sessions
could be shortened. After several months of such
practice, Luthe maintains that a state of altered
consciousness, with profound physical relaxation, can be
induced by simply thinking: *Heaviness — warmth —
heartbeat* and *respiration — solar plexus — forehead.*

Be that as it may, many people will not be interested in such rigorous training. Others may like the systematic nature of the formulas. However, whether you do practise systematically or not, the idea of using your imagination to feel heavy and warm, with your heartbeat and breathing being calm and regular, cannot help but induce a more physically relaxed state. It will also help create mental calmness.

Mental relaxation

Most forms of mental relaxation involve imagining yourself to be in some pleasant place. Practising this is best done when you are not under stress, so that you can make a game out of it, letting your mind drift into many such places until you find the one or ones which calm you most effectively. The place might change according to the weather. A pleasant place on a very hot day might be floating around a swimming pool on an inflatable mattress. On a very cold day, it might be sitting in a comfortable chair before a roaring log fire. That is the beauty of your imagination. You can go wherever you want to go. Develop a number of these fantasies and keep them in the 'jewel box' of your mind, ready to be brought forth when you need to relax mentally.

Though you have to develop your own peaceful environments, it may help to know of some images that other people use. One of the most popular is that of lying on the beach in summertime, enjoying the warmth of the sun soaking into the body, the sound of the water lapping on the sand, the taste of the salt and the cries of the gulls. It is possible to feel your body sinking down into the sand, becoming increasingly heavy and relaxed.

Sand can be used in another way too. Imagine that your body is full of sand. There is a little hole somewhere, perhaps in your foot, through which the sand slowly trickles away, taking with it the tension in your mind and body.

A hole, though a bigger one this time, plays a part in

another fantasy which is used for calming the mind. Think of a rubber ball bouncing back from a wall. Now, imagine a hole in the wall through which the ball can bounce. Be that hole yourself, offering no resistance to the cause of the emotional disturbance that you may feel. Everything passes through the hole that is you, unable to disturb your equanimity.

Rather than being passive in this way, you might like to actively take control. If so, the following fantasy may appeal to you. Visualize yourself standing before a control panel which has one large dial. This dial can be turned to any setting from zero to ten, representing all the levels of tension and relaxation which your mind and body can experience. Zero is the complete relaxation end of the dial, and you can turn it down to that point if you wish. As you turn the dial down, feel all mental tension draining away. This is, of course, very similar to the 'comfort' scale described in the previous chapter. However, some people find the dial easier to imagine than the scale.

Others may find another simple 'action' image useful in creating mental calm. Imagine that you are standing on a ledge overlooking a quiet pool. Visualize yourself lifting a large heavy rock over your head. Drop it into the pool. Watch the rock as it enters the water, seeing the splash in slow motion and the rock slowly sinking to the bottom. As it does so, imagine the water closing in above it, the rings of water rippling out all over the pool surface. Watch the ripples until they die away, leaving the surface glassy smooth once again.

Gardens are another popular calming image. Tracy Ballentine, a rather nervous operating-room Sister who came to me to seek a way of relaxing mentally, uses a rather effective one. She imagines herself standing on the patio of a lovely old house. From this patio, a flight of ten steps leads down to a beautiful sunken garden. As she breathes out, Tracy goes down one step, letting go a little each time that she does so. By the time she reaches the garden, she has already released much of her mental tension.

The garden is beautiful, with masses of flowers — red, blue, and gold — and shrubs, an ornamental fountain, trees, and birds. Tracy not only sees these things, but imagines that she can smell the flowers, hear the birds and the splashing of the water into the pool at the base of the fountain, as well as feel the warm sun soaking into her body. Also, she uses one of the trees as her strength image — a concept which was explained earlier in the second chapter.

What Tracy is doing is hypnotizing herself into a state of calm. At times she does this more formally by using different imagery. She begins by sitting comfortably and focusing her eyes upon a spot ahead of, and a little above, her line of vision. As her eyes become tired and as her vision blurs, Tracy lets them shut, imagining as she does so that a warm cloud is bathing the centre of her body. As this cloud touches any part of her body, it warms and relaxes that part.

Tracy then imagines the cloud slowly expanding from her centre, growing larger and larger, touching each part of her body in turn with its energy, warmth, and peace. This total immersion in a revitalizing cloud releases all internal tension.

Once Tracy is completely engulfed in the cloud, she imagines that her body becomes lighter, warmer and calmer — so that it seems to float weightlessly upwards, soaring into the sky. Safely cushioned within the centre of the cloud, she is taken to her special garden. After enjoying the tranquility of this place, Tracy descends in her cloud, returns to her chair, and enjoys the aftermath of peace and calm. She is often able to keep it with her for the rest of the day.

Meditation as a mental relaxation

Though Tracy's cloud fantasy and her eye-fixation preliminary could be labelled as self-hypnosis, they could just as easily be termed meditation. Not that labels really matter. As long as we achieve the result that we want, what particular label we use does not seem all that important. Tracy's husband, Ron, uses something which he calls 'action meditation' to create mental calm because he is not interested in sitting down to fantasize. As he goes for his morning run along the beach, he breathes in the world around him, paying attention to the sensations arising from his environment. As he breathes out, he is aware of himself as being present in these sensations. He makes no attempt to control his breathing in any way, but simply shifts his attention from the world to himself as he inhales and exhales. Ron breathes in air — and takes in the world; he breathes out air — and is aware of himself, calm and serene.

Though this is his favourite meditation, he also uses an internally focused one which, he says, separates his mind from his body. This separation enables him to run long distances without even realizing it. Ron locates a space in the toe of his left foot, the bone of his left foot, the bone of his left ankle, the toe of his right foot, and so on through the entire body. Or, perhaps, he focuses longer on the big toe of his left foot, sensing the inside of it, the skin around it, the space between it and the next toe. This takes quite a long time; and Ron claims that while he is mentally occupied in this way he cannot worry about anything else.

Another meditation which he uses to achieve a state of mental calm involves concentration upon sound. Ron focuses on one particular sound. He does not attempt to label it. Instead he analyzes it. Is it high or low, sharp or dull, loud or soft? As that sound fades away, another takes its place. As it does, Ron analyzes it in the same detached fashion. In this way he preserves a certain calmness of mind. Actually, this is an excellent way of dealing with a noisy environment. Analyze the sound, not the person or the thing making it.

A most effective meditation to induce both deep

mental relaxation and a sense of appreciation for being alive is one described by Brugh Joy in his book *Joy's Way*. This is a spiral meditation, involving key body energy centres called 'chakras'. The position of these are illustrated.

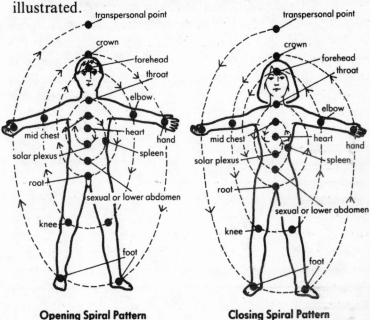

Opening Spiral Pattern   **Closing Spiral Pattern**

To begin on the opening spiral, centre your awareness in the heart chakra area, leaving personal concerns behind. As you do so, it is likely that you will become aware of a feeling of warmth, expansion or vibration in that area and, once you can feel this sensation, carry it with you to the solar plexus, focusing on this area until it, too, is warm and vibrant. Repeat the process, going to each successive chakra in the spiral, waiting until it feels activated, and then moving on. It is not unusual to create a really blissful feeling as you do this, a feeling that remains as you arrive at the transpersonal point and relax into the meditative state. When you are ready to leave this state, work through the spiral in the opposite direction. When you reach the heart chakra again, revel in a sense of expanded appreciation for the opportunity to be alive.

Using self-hypnosis

Although I have written of body relaxation and mind relaxation under different headings, it is impossible to separate the two. Most relaxation techniques have as their aim both the calming of the mind and the release of physical tension. Usually, when your muscles relax, so too will your mind, and vice versa. Often this state is labelled self-hypnosis.

Some actual techniques for inducing self-hypnosis have been explained in the second chapter, when I described how to induce trance states. At that time I pointed out that a formal induction is not really necessary because, each day, we drift in and out of self-hypnotic states. Just closing our eyes, letting go our muscles, and allowing our attention to drift in the direction of a pleasant memory is as easy a way as any. Another simple way that children enjoy is to imagine themselves as eagles, flying from one peaceful place to another. When anything disturbs them, they simply fly off to some happier, safer place.

Some of us enjoy more formalized methods. We have a certain sense of security in having a set formula which can be repeated as a ritual to induce our self-hypnotic state. One which I particularly like is described in *Trance-formations* by Grinder and Bandler. It goes like this:

- Before commencing, fix a time of 'awakening'. Visualize a clockface in your mind with the time for completing your session shown on it.
- Find something easy to look at. Gaze at it and say to yourself three sentences about what you see — e.g. 'I see the light glittering on a piece of cut glass'. 'I see ...' 'I see ...' Then switch to three sentences about what you can hear — e.g. 'I hear the sound of a door shutting'. 'I hear ...' 'I hear ...' Next comes three sentences about what you feel — e.g. 'I feel the pressure of the chair against my back'. 'I feel ...' 'I feel ...'

- Maintaining the same position in your chair and the same direction of your gaze, go through the 'I see', 'I hear', 'I feel', again, this time saying two sentences for each. Repeat once again, this time with one sentence for each. You may find that as you do this your eyes become too heavy to keep open, so the 'I see ...' part drops out and you use only 'I hear ...' and 'I feel ...'.

- Sense whichever of your arms feel lighter, then suggest that it will continue to feel increasingly light until it floats into the air towards your face. When it touches your face, let your arm flop down and go into a deep trance.

- Decide on whatever it is about your experience that you want to alter. For example, you may want to be more patient. Ask your unconscious mind to review with sound, feeling, and images those past situations when you acted patiently. Then ask your unconscious mind, when it is finished making this review, to extract the vital elements of these situations and have them occur, naturally and spontaneously, more and more frequently in your everyday behaviour.

This technique is one which I would recommend very highly. It can lead to great changes in your behaviour, changes which you have decided would be of benefit to you. So, this approach can achieve a lot more for you than creating a sense of relaxation. Of course, the other methods that I have talked about in this chapter also give benefits over and above those of relaxation. Many of these relate to health and healing, so we will look at this aspect more closely in the next chapter.

8 Healing Through the Imagination

Self-health training

One very useful way of employing relaxation procedures to promote healing is through 'biogenics' or 'self-health training', a five-step system proposed by the famous neurosurgeon Norman Shealy:

- *Relax.* As you breathe in, repeat 'I am ...'; as you breathe out, repeat '... relaxed'.
- *Balance your body feelings.* Tune in to each part of the body and note whether it is relaxed. If not, consciously let go that area by:
  - (a) mentally feeling the heartbeat in that area, or
  - (b) tensing and loosening muscles, or
  - (c) imagining you are breathing through that area.
- *Balance your emotions.* Consciously examine fear, anger, guilt, and making a decision to resolve the problem and create emotional joy, happiness, compassion, forgiveness, and love.
- *Programme yourself to accomplish a goal.*
  - (a) *Verbally* with a short, positive healing mantra repeated frequently which expresses a goal as if it is already accomplished — e.g. 'My blood pressure is normal'.
  - (b) *Visually* with a visual image of yourself as having accomplished the goal — e.g. by seeing yourself in the doctor's surgery as he tells you your blood pressure is normal.

- *Become spiritually attuned.* Be aware that you are something beyond body, mind, and emotion. Tune in to your magnificent inner self or essence.

Imagination plays an important part in this healing system of Shealy's, which he claims has been extremely successful with patients suffering from many different health problems.

Using the imagination to promote healing

For thousands of years, visualization has been used to promote self-healing. Many studies have demonstrated that imagery which is both seen and felt can substantially affect brain waves, blood flow, heart rate, skin temperature, gastric secretions, and the immune response. It really appears as if our whole physiology can be influenced by our imagination.

The principle involved is one of imagining, while in a relaxed state, the malfunctioning organ or part of the body operating at its best. Should you be attempting to counter an infection, you could imagine white blood cells, visualized as cells, little soldiers, worker ants, or as some comic-dreadful creature moving in on the infection, breaking it up and carrying it off to be flushed out of the system. As you hold in your mind a new image of your system functioning in a healthy way, you might speak directly to your unconscious mind, requesting it to continue the healing process. Children find this quite easy to do. One child I know, when he had the misfortune to break a bone in his wrist, accelerated his healing by imagining little animals putting bone cement in the crack.

Creating and using healing imagery seems so simple that many people find it difficult to believe that it could actually help them. Yet, tissue repair and regeneration are processes that the body does for itself. Though a doctor may adjust a bone, or try to control pain and infection, it is the body that must accomplish the healing. Apparently, relaxation and imagery can enhance these natural healing processes.

In *Healing From Within*, Denis Jaffe describes the first occasion on which he was exposed to the power of healing imagery. This was through an accident which happened to his friend, Mark. As a result of a head-on automobile crash, Mark had both legs crushed, one of them nearly severed below the knee and broken in many places. Apparently the pain was so excruciating that pain medication was becoming ineffective. Though his physicians recommended amputation of both legs because there was virtually no hope of them ever healing, Mark refused surgery. He did so in the face of the diagnosis that he would never walk again and could expect a lifetime of severe leg pain.

As the pain mounted over ensuing weeks, a healer taught Mark to relax and to spend most of his waking hours telling the legs to heal. He was to imagine his broken bones joining and his infections healing. Further, he visualized himself walking naturally. This is, in fact, exactly what happened. Within two years, Mark was walking with only a slight limp, a recovery which his physicians described as 'unprecedented'.

Jaffe believes that Mark mobilized some innate, latent, and potent healing mechanism through his relaxation and the instructions which he gave to his body. We all have this power, Jaffe suggests. To invoke it, we should begin with deep relaxation. Then, we create a mental image of what we want our bodies to do. If we are technically minded we might like to read some medical texts, which enable us to create very precise images. Should we not choose to do this, we may like to use symbolic or fanciful images. Apparently, according to physicians using these methods, it does not seem to matter how realistic the images are. So, we may visualize our bodies producing an extra supply of a particular enzyme or, instead, imagine rays of light energizing our bodies, or, more fanciful still, little men with ray guns charging through our bodies, killing an oozy green virus. All three images will probably produce similar results.

The key is to feel comfortable with the healing imagery which you choose to use. If you let images come spontaneously, this will usually happen automatically. Try this now. Relax. Focus your mind on any part of your body where you feel discomfort. Experience this discomfort fully. Allow a picture related to that body part to drift into your mind. Now, visualize a process taking place within this image, causing that part of your body to become more comfortable and to function better. Hold this picture in your mind for five or ten minutes. Meditate on it. If your attention wanders bring it back to your healing image. Perhaps the picture will change. Let it. Follow it whichever way it becomes transformed. Keep this focus on your healing image over the ensuing weeks, perhaps spending a few minutes several times a day doing so. Probably, the image will keep re-occurring spontaneously. Become aware of it when this happens, then let it go, allowing your unconscious mind to continue its healing work and to be constantly stimulated by your image.

It has been suggested that much of the healing power of our imagery is due to its stimulation of the body's immune system. This self-protection network helps us deal with specific invaders which break through the skin or enter our bodies either in the air we breathe or the food we eat. When activated, our immune system sends various protective substances, such as white blood cells and lymphocytes, through the blood stream and lymph system, to the site of the danger. The body then manufactures other substances which enable it to destroy the invader — be it a virus, bacteria, or some other foreign body. Thus, by imagining, say, large white blood cells multiplying and rushing to the site of the infection, it seems that we are stimulating our bodies to protect us more effectively.

Healing imagery

Though we are best served when we provide our own images, it is helpful to consider how those used by others would suit us. Jenny Vertigan, an avid gardener, uses an image very close to her heart. Above her head, she pictures a red rose which is beautifully shaped and vibrant with colour. On the top of the rose is a drop of moisture. This has positively magical qualities. It rolls off the rose petals, landing on Jenny's head and soaks through her until it reaches the area of discomfort which it commences to heal.

One of Jenny's friends, Mary, closes her eyes and lets her disease symptoms become bubbles. Mary then imagines these bubbles being blown out of her mind, out of her body, and out of her consciousness by a breeze. The bubbles are drawn away into the distance until she no longer feels them. They disappear over the horizon. They are no more.

To clear her eyes of pain Mary uses a rather different form of imagery. She draws mentally, a big black circle, putting dots on either side. It looks like this:

Mary moves her attention from one black dot to the other, back and forth again and again, until the circle seems to shift. It seems to move out of the way as Mary's eyes shift between the dots. Her eyes relax, her vision improves and the pain tends to be forgotten.

Another healing image that Mary finds helpful involves a globe of bright light. She images this globe hovering over her body, sending out rays of warmth and healing which penetrate every fibre of her being. Once she feels this happening, she imagines that the sphere slowly descends, merging with her mind and body so that the rays radiate outward from within, forming a glowing shield which heals very deeply.

Such images of light and warmth are used frequently by many people. Often they are linked to a focus on the solar plexus. This body centre, from which nerves radiate to all abdominal organs, is so important for effective body functioning that imagery designed to facilitate its action is likely to produce good results. Place your hand over the upper part of your abdomen, feeling a sensation of pleasant warmth soaking and penetrating into the solar plexus, regulating its function. This can be done by imagining a solar plexus timer such as a speedometer, or a clock, which indicates a 'correct setting'. At this setting, all organs will operate normally. So, if you have abdominal troubles, menstrual problems, spastic colon, bowel difficulties, or morning sickness, regulate your solar plexus timer so that it shows the 'correct setting'. Imagine the nerves radiating out to the area of discomfort, carrying soothing, healing impulses. This particular imagery has proven quite successful in helping bed-wetters solve their problems and it can sometimes produce spectacular results in the overcoming of travel sickness.

Of great importance in the use of such techniques is the imagining of a positive future outcome. This counters the initial negative beliefs and expectations which a person usually has. Seeing yourself healthy, together with other positive self-guided imagery, helps by creating hope, and also by giving a sufferer something constructive to do instead of waiting passively for treatment to take effect. Imagining a successful outcome, because of the gentleness of its action, is more likely to prove effective than trying to will or force yourself to do something.

One way of doing this and, in addition, of increasing the power of any healing method that you are using, is the split-screen technique. Visualize a large screen, somewhat akin to that used in drive-in theatres. The screen is to be divided into three segments. Initially on the right-hand segment you see yourself as you are. Thus, should the problem be one of a sprained ankle, you would see yourself with this injury, immobilized, and in pain.

The right-hand segment of the screen then goes dark as you 'turn off' the picture of yourself as you are, with your swollen, inflamed ankle. The centre segment of the screen is the next to be used as you visualize the treatment which will heal the injury. This may involve using ice packs for the first 24 hours and then the application of heat. You might also visualize taking a homoeopathic remedy such as Arnica, the virtues of which I have outlined in *The Healing Factor*.

As you 'black out' this centre segment, visualize yourself, on the right-hand segment, as you would like to be. You are moving comfortably, your ankle free of all swelling and inflammation.

By imaging the desired end point, whether it be good health or a life goal, and allowing the unconscious mind to take you there without interference from the conscious mind, you tap powerful resources within you. These may be visualized in terms of an inner advisor or source of wisdom.

The inner advisor

By creating and interacting with an inner advisor, you can learn to gather important information from your unconscious mind and to become increasingly comfortable with those parts of yourself which were previously inaccessible to conscious awareness. Thus you build a dialogue between your conscious and unconscious selves. Quite often you may discover feelings that you have not faced, or some source of conflict in your life that has weakened your resistance, making you susceptible to a particular ailment.

Although it may be a difficult concept to accept, it appears as if our body, our unconscious potentials, our needs and functions, all operate within us as if they had minds of their own. Though they affect our behaviour, we are often not aware of what is happening. This is why the reframing procedure described in the third chapter can produce startling results. It is useful to be aware of such techniques for it is not an easy task to bring together the various hidden parts of ourselves.

As Jaffe has pointed out in *Healing From Within*, healing of many serious illnesses follows quickly upon 'a realization that a part of oneself has been denied, forgotten, ignored, rejected, or despised'. Some form of internal dialogue may provide the means of learning about such rejection, permitting a re-integration leading to better health. Such a dialogue can be carried on in many ways. Jaffe quotes the case of a patient who used letters to communicate with her cancer:

> I began to write letters to my cancer as a way of communicating with it. I have learned that whatever we hate, we give power to, and it has the power to hurt us. But when we make friends with our problem, it will not hurt us. Besides, we cannot reject something and simply turn it over to God. We must first accept it, because, after all, we made it happen to us.
>
> I wrote down what I felt about my cancer, and then I wrote what my cancer said to me. I managed to discover a great deal about myself, and how I keep my real needs inside me and do not ask others to help me. I don't think I would have discovered these things in any other way than by having cancer. It's too bad the lessons of our life have to be so harsh, but at least I finally paid attention to things. I hope you will learn to take care of yourself as well.

In this case, it seems as if the lady's cancer may well have been the result of a lifetime of systematic self-denial. She used her cancer as an inner advisor, to help her understand herself. Talking to our illness can be a very fruitful dialogue, in that we are using it as an internal voice which tells us what we are doing wrong in our lives. It can also tell us what to do to improve matters.

Another of Jaffe's cases was that of a nurse born with a hip deformity. She would pay particular attention to the needs of her hips and legs. When she felt discomfort, she would ask her tight muscles what she could do to take care of them. 'Massage us' or 'Take a day off and read' they would reply, through a 'voice in her head'. She would also use bargaining. If she needed to do something especially active, such as spending a day sailing, she would say to her hips: 'If you let me do this without much pain, in return I will take special care to rest you for the next two days. Is that all right?' Then she would wait for an answer. Peculiar as this might seem, it enabled the nurse to live a relatively pain-free life for many years. After all, if such a procedure, peculiar or not, makes life easier, it seems very worthwhile.

Although it is not unusual for people to use their own illness as an inner advisor, it is more common for the guide to be a person, an animal, or a thing. There are a multitude of ways of using the imagination to create such a guide. One fantasy, developed by Jean Houston in *The Possible Human*, involves your initial physical relaxation and then imagining that you are on a mountain top looking for a way down. You notice steps cut out of rock winding their way around and down the mountain. These you follow though the way may be difficult and rough. When you reach the foot of the mountain, you see a door leading inside. This you enter to find yourself in a long corridor. You feel quite at ease, for the corridor provides an atmosphere of safety and security.

As you follow the passage deeper into the mountain, you notice that the walls have pictures portraying a variety of glorious nature scenes. You are surrounded by beautiful rock and cellular formations on all sides. At the end of the corridor is a door. On it are the words: 'The One Who Knows Health'. You open the door and go in to meet this being.

This is someone or something who understands all about you — the one who is the representative of your own body wisdom and has access to vast information concerning your state of health and what is necessary for its improvement. Sit down in the chair across from this being. Ask questions, both specific and general, about yourself. Do not demand answers. Wait quietly. Be receptive to whatever comes. The One Who Knows Health may communicate in words, images, muscular sensations, or feeling states.

When you sense that the messages have finished, ask the Wise One: 'What can I do for you?' Sit quietly in deep communion, meditating on the answer you get. Finally, thank the being for the wisdom offered, leave, close the door behind you, retrace your steps, and integrate the new knowledge that you have gained, until you arrive back at the mountain top. Open your eyes, letting the fantasy go, knowing now that you can return to gain further wisdom whenever it seems necessary.

Often, the information that you gain from such internal dialogues will relate to your energy level as well as to any particular illness which you may have. It is possible to use your imagination to generate increased energy just as it is possible to use it for the promotion of healing.

Generating energy

Tim Anders, a mechanic who would appear to be the most practical and down-to-earth of men, is someone who uses his fertile imagination most effectively to boost his energy level when it seems to be flagging. He imagines himself enveloped in white light, lying on a comfortable bed. By the bed is a table on which rests a glass of water. This is very special water for it contains the universal energy, the ultimate life force. As Tim gazes into the water, he can see an image of outer space. When he drinks, he imagines he is drawing on infinite power, feeling it coursing through him to every part of his body in turn.

With this imagery, Tim is using his mind as a

transformer. He draws in the energy and healing power of the universe, directing it to wherever it is needed, either inwardly to his own body or outwardly towards other people. For Tim has found that he has the ability to energize and heal other people. He discovered this ability almost by accident — confirming my own belief that most of us are capable of healing others. However, we need confidence in ourselves, a real belief that we can help other people in this way. Using the power of imagination to draw on outside forces, whether they be 'universal energy' or something else, often helps us achieve this confidence in our healing powers.

Belief in the power of our centre located below the navel can also help in this regard. You can think of this area as a centre of energy and life force. Because the major muscles are attached there, efficient movement begins in our centre. So, we can imagine transforming virtually anything into energy by breathing it down into our centre. Recognize that it is all energy, whether it be manifested as the anxiety over being left alone, or the uneasiness of meeting strangers, or the irritability over the flat tyre. Realize that the tightly clenched jaw, the eyelid twitch, the furrowed brow, and the nervously tapping finger are all energy fragments, ready to be made whole again. Breathe them down into your centre, transform them, and use them in positive ways.

As you inhale, concentrate on drawing in energy through your nose, down through your throat and your heart to your lower abdomen centre where you store it. As you exhale, direct energy to your body parts one at a time, letting the fatigue melt away. Perhaps you see the incoming energy as luminous white light, regenerating your body, and the fatigue that you release as a black cloud, soon to disappear completely. The concept of an energy scale can be helpful, too. As you breathe in the luminous white light, imagine that you increase one step or one half-step on your zero-to-ten scale. Lift yourself to the desired level, then let the image go and experience the energy that you have created for yourself.

Do not underestimate the value of imagining a scale for whatever it is with which you are concerned. One of the greatest benefits that such an image can bestow is with pain relief, an area which we consider in the next chapter.

9 Pain Management

The scale image

In terms of pain management, two scales are very useful. The first of these relates to the actual pain sensation itself. Ask yourself: 'If I could rate my pain on a zero-to-ten scale, where is the pain right now? What is the most pain I have had with this particular health problem? Where on the scale is the average pain in a day?' The second aspect of pain is suffering, or how much bother it causes. You can ask yourself the same three questions, substituting 'how much bother' for 'how much pain'.

In a relaxed state, see the number of the scale that you hurt at this moment. Watch it carefully because the number you see is the amount of pain you feel. That number is going to get smaller and smaller. Imagine this happening. As the number does become smaller, experience an increase in comfort. Continue reducing the number. See it happening until you arrive at the number one.

Because pain is a signal that something is wrong with your body, and you need to know this, it is wise to leave some small amount remaining. Through use of this method you should be able to improve things for yourself considerably. You will achieve some pain reduction but you really will not know how much. You might need to repeat the procedure a number of times but, on the other hand, you might not. The same process may be followed to reduce the degree of bother produced by the pain, or you may find some of the other approaches to be now described more suitable.

What imaginary situation suits you best?

You will find it helpful to try out several different pain-reduction approaches to ascertain which works best for you. You may like to experiment with any of the relaxation or trance-induction methods sprinkled so liberally through these pages. Once relaxed, imagine that you are in the dentist's chair or in any other situation where you expect to experience pain. If your muscles tense, repeat the relaxation procedure, and then imagine yourself in some peaceful situation.

This is one way of going about it. Another is, once you have relaxed, to picture yourself engaged in some exciting, arousing activity. You may be water-skiing, driving fast along a winding road, surfing, dancing, or doing anything else which stimulates you. Becoming engrossed in action may be a better 'turn-off' of the negative dental chair imagery than is the passivity of the peaceful scene.

Or, perhaps, pretending that you are your favourite hero or heroine might work even better. Relax, think of yourself in the dental chair, then 'switch off' and become a famous athlete, a brilliant surgeon, an orchestra conductor, a 'pop' singer with an audience of thousands, or someone else whom you admire.

Actually, one of the fastest 'cures' which I ever effected used a variant of this approach. A 13-year-old son of a friend of mine was a bed-wetter. On one occasion, I was chatting to this boy while waiting for his father to finish a telephone call. He was talking about football, and about the player whom he most admired. I asked him quite seriously whether he thought this man wet his bed at night. The lad was absolutely shocked at the very idea. We continued to talk of other things for a few minutes more, then I rejoined his father. Apparently, the boy began having more dry beds from this time on, and within three weeks he had virtually 'cured' himself of his bed-wetting behaviour.

So, using a hero and a heroine can be a powerful way of changing behaviour. Another imaginary situation which is applicable to the dental chair is to think of relaxing at home, lying on your bed, and listening to someone using the vacuum cleaner in the next room. The sound of the vacuum is coming closer and closer. In fact, it almost seems to be in your mouth, but that does not matter. You can stay comfortably relaxed thinking about what you are going to do later in the day.

The idea of using sound as well as pictures is likely to be very useful to you in many situations. Let's apply it again to the dental chair example. You are sitting in the chair as the dentist prepares to work on your mouth. First, think about what you would be doing if you were not there at the dentist's surgery. If that is not very interesting, use one of the images suggested earlier in this chapter. Once you have the picture firmly in your mind, imagine that you can, at the same time, hear music. Perhaps, it is a radio playing or a tape. Beat time to the music on the arm of the chair. Concentrate only on what you want to see and hear, the picture and the music, so that whatever the dentist is doing in your mouth fades into insignificance.

By shifting your attention away from your mouth, you dampen down any pain. When we concentrate on what the dentist is doing to us, which is what we usually do, we amplify any pain through our own anxiety. The effect of this dampening or amplifying can be seen with burns patients. If a person who is burnt remains relatively calm, or is able to shift mentally so that he or she does not attend to the burn area, the skin may react only minimally. That is, the burn will be limited precisely to where the stimulus touched the skin. On the other hand, should the person be especially anxious, concerned about, and focusing strongly on the sensations of burning and pain, he or she can increase the extent and depth of skin damage produced by the burn stimulus. So, it really comes down again to the necessity of engaging in a variety of mental activities which serve the purpose of distracting attention from the pain.

Distraction through use of the imagination

Geraldine Eggleston, an elderly lady with a long history of painful illnesses, has over the years learnt to distance herself from her suffering. One of the ways in which she does so involves shifting her concentration from the area of pain to another body area. Each time she feels discomfort, she focuses on the exquisite sensations present in the fingers of her left hand. Geraldine rubs these fingers one against the other, describing to herself the texture, the temperature, and any other sensations which she feels. Whenever she is tempted to concentrate on her pain, she rubs her fingers together gently to provide an alternate focus of awareness.

On other occasions she will rest her fingertips lightly on her solar plexus, or leave them just slightly above it. Geraldine then imagines white light being drawn up into her fingers, charging them with energy until the fingertips seem to vibrate with the power they hold. She places her fingertips just above or on the source of pain, imagining the white light streaming down into the area, spreading its healing warmth.

Often this procedure has the effect of producing a numbness which is infinitely preferable to pain. In fact, many people have found ways of using their imagination to create a sense of numbness in painful body areas. You could imagine yourself in a bathtub filled with ice, which cools your body to such an extent that it will be impervious to discomfort. Or else visualize yourself placing a glass of icy cold water against the painful area so that all feeling is drawn out by the water acting as a magnet.

We are used to the sensation of numbness which follows an injection of novacaine. You can create the same effect through the use of your imagination. Visualize the needle being inserted painlessly in the damaged area. Feel a dulling sensation at the point of insertion, then a gradually increasing sense of numbness as the novocaine exerts its effect, eliminating all pain.

Perhaps the novocaine could be injected into your hand so that it falls asleep, feeling as if it is quite inert, like a block of wood or as if it is encased in a leather gauntlet. You can then transfer this feeling to any other part of your body by touching it and allowing the numbness to flow from your fingers into the painful area.

By numbing a painful body part in this way, it is as if you were disassociating yourself from it. This is what Geraldine does when, for instance, she receives an injection. A needle is not being placed in her arm. It is inserted into *an* arm. In imagination, she moves outside her body and looks at this arm from a distance. Because she detaches herself in this way, Geraldine sees her arm as an object. It is virtually as if the needle was being inserted into the arm of a chair.

This concept of disassociation can be taken further. On some occasions, Geraldine will visualize another person dressed like her, looking like her, who is receiving the treatment and experiencing the pain. No discomfort touches *her*, however. It is this 'other woman' who suffers. However, while the 'other woman' undergoes treatment, Geraldine may also busy herself, letting her gaze roam slowly across the ceiling, down one wall, over the window curtains and around the pattern in the fabric. This combines distraction with disassociation — a powerful combination because it seems as if pain is primarily composed both of fear of pain and of paying attention to it. Through her distancing methods, and her provision of concentration points other than that of the pain, Geraldine has lost much of her fear. Thus she has lost much of her pain.

Sometimes she will use her 'magic blanket'. Through the use of her imagination Geraldine has created a gossamer-light and beautiful-looking blanket with magical properties. She visualizes this being placed over her legs from knees to feet. Gradually she loses all sense of feeling in her legs as the pain is absorbed by the blanket. Soon she is no longer conscious of her legs and feet. The blanket is unfolded a little more. Now it covers her thighs and hips, once again absorbing all pain. This it continues to do until the blanket is drawn up snugly beneath her chin. Now, she is free to 'leave her body' and imagine herself in a place where she is relaxed and happy, completely free of pain, and totally unaware of her body.

Turning off the switches

Another person who controls his pain well is Roger Pearson. His right hand is the problem, for he has very painful arthritis. Initially he attempted to use a pain-relief technique which had proven successful during visits to the dentist. On these occasions, he was able to imagine a cool, comfortable fog touching his cheeks, being breathed in, and pleasantly numbing his tongue, mouth and throat. However, when Roger tried to breathe this numbing fog into his hand, it did not give him the relief that he expected.

Next, he used a dissassociation technique. This consisted of imagining that he unscrewed his hand so that it was no longer part of him. This did not work either, pointing up the fact that the method that is successful for one person will not necessarily be so for someone else. Both the numbing fog and the unscrewed hand have worked well for other people whom I know.

Roger's third attempt was more successful. He visualized wire-like nerves running from his hand, winding up the length of his arm and through his shoulder and neck. As they came closer to the brain, the wires became thicker, enabling them to carry more information. At their thickest part, just before they entered the brain, they went through a switchbox equipped with a lever for turning 'current' on or off. The off position stops any signal from passing through the wire.

Roger embellished this image. He imagined his skin as transparent so that he could see bones, blood vessels and muscles. The fine wires of his nerves were very small as they began in his fingertips, becoming bigger as they passed through his hand, and thicker still by the time they reached his elbow. Roger imagined them as being blue in colour. They passed through his spine, the back of his neck, and into the black switchbox in the middle of his head. Although he now uses only a single lever to turn off the 'current' of his pain, he originally imagined a row of switches in his black box. Under each switch was a little sign showing which part of the body it controlled. Roger would turn off the switch controlling his hand. However, after he became more used to this technique he preferred using the lever as a master switch, turning off discomfort everywhere in his body.

An alternative way of employing this kind of pain-relief image is to visualize the area of affliction connected with the control centre in the brain by a highway-like strand of wires along which the message of pain travels. Somewhere between these two points, imagine a road-block of some description. Visualize the pain energies streaming out of the diseased area and coming to a halt at the roadblock, leaving the rest of the road empty of pain messages. Thus, the control centre cannot receive the impulses carrying pain. The power of this imagery may be increased if coupled with verbal suggestions that the pain is unable to penetrate the roadblock.

Yet another variation on this theme is to visualize your injury in great detail, then seal it off in some way. You may build a protective wall around it, or encase it in a bubble of light, or imagine it encircled by a blue neon glow. Whatever imagery you use, the idea is to create a protective shield so that the nerve fibres leading from the affected area to the brain carry no pain messages.

All these variants work on the concept of blocking off pain impulses from the brain so that you become unaware of discomfort. Strangely enough, taking the opposite tack of actually concentrating on your pain can also bring relief.

Directing attention to your pain

Carol Higgins, a working mother with three children, is subject to severe pain in her back. At one time, she had gained some measure of control over her pain through disassociation. She would see 'another person', dressed the same and looking the same as she was, feeling the pain. She herself was separated from the discomfort. Further, this 'other person' had in her brain the switches mentioned in the last section. In Carol's case, these had three positions: 'up' to increase pain, 'centre' to maintain pain, and 'down' to reduce pain. The idea here is that Carol could imagine the 'other person' taking control over her pain, varying its intensity at will and being able to increase or decrease the sensitivity of any part of the body.

This approach helped Carol for well over a year, but gradually its effectiveness in reducing her pain diminished. This occurred both when the 'other person' used the switches and when she used them herself. This is an important point. It is rare that things are perfect and last forever. Something we find marvellous at one time becomes less than wonderful at another time. When we first find something that seems to tremendously enhance our lives we are ecstatic. We've found the answer. Yet, probably the secret of life is that there is no secret. We can use whatever works well for us but must be flexible, ready to try something else if its effectiveness wanes.

This is what Carol had to do. Her alternative approach came almost by accident. On the relatively few occasions when she imagined herself moving her own switches into the 'up' position, Carol actually felt her pain reduce rather than increase. This surprised her greatly, but it began to make more sense when she read a magazine article about a therapeutic technique called paradoxical intention. Using this method, a patient is encouraged to do the very thing that he or she fears. A stutterer, for example, would deliberately try to stutter more than ever. Peculiarly enough, the harder he or she tries to do so, the more fluently he or she may speak. Similarly, a person afraid of vomiting can often help himself or herself by actually trying hard to vomit.

Carol thought that something like this may have happened with her pain. On the next occasion when her back ached, she concentrated upon it, giving it her full attention, enhancing and intensifying it. To herself, she described it in detail. Was it more on one side of the back than on the other? Was it a large or a small pain? Was it heavy or light? What colour was it? Did it seem to move from one place to another? Was it hot or cold?

As I have mentioned earlier (in Chapter 6), you can use such a detailed survey as a precursor to changing something. Pain relief may be effected by, for example, changing the colour of the pain to some other colour associated with comfort, and a burning sensation can be reduced through the use of imaginary ice packs.

Colour change can be incorporated into quite elaborate fantasies. Carol used one of these. As she gave full attention to her pain, localizing it exactly, she imagined herself being in a room with a bridge across its centre. Standing on this bridge was like being on the inside of a globe, with coloured maps of the world on the surrounding walls. However, in Carol's case, the maps were of her pain, with the colour red showing its intensity and concentration as well as the exact area covered. Carol imagined that a diluting agent was being put into the red so that it began to fade a little, turning paler. Some neutralization took place, as if the pain was being washed out, rendered increasingly harmless. It looked better.

Actually, Carol now uses this imagery to do more than reduce pain. By examining her pain from the inside, so to speak, she is sometimes able to see what is beside it, around it, within it. She may see when it began, when it recurs, to whom or to what it is related, and other valuable information similar to that which is available from the hidden advisor (as referred to in Chapter 8).

On one occasion when she was in hospital recovering from an operation on her back, Carol found that her map fantasy was not achieving sufficient pain reduction. As I have previously mentioned, the effectiveness of the various imaginative techniques mentioned do tend to fluctuate. At this time, she made use of another disassociation technique which is of particular value when a person is bedridden. Whenever Carol felt that she could not tolerate her pain, she 'left' her body in bed, imagining her head and shoulder being placed in a wheel chair. This was then wheeled into another room. There she could watch a fascinating series of special television programmes for as long as she desired. She could then return to join the rest of her body which had endured the pain without her actually being aware of it.

This was a technique which Carol had used earlier in her life during the birth of her two children. At those times she visualized either actual television programmes or the birth itself taking place on the screen. Any reader who, like Carol, enjoys television will find this a very useful method indeed. It is well suited to situations such as childbirth, and it is worth noting that particular techniques do seem appropriate to particular problems. This is something we take up in the next chapter.

10 Specific Problem Areas

The virtue of simplicity

Carol's methods of reducing pain worked well most of the time. However, some readers may feel unable or unwilling to use imagery which is as complex as hers. This is quite a reasonable view, and there are many virtues in simplicity. It is easy to become overly complex in our approach to the problems in our lives. Often, a very simple approach will be more effective and far easier to put into practice.

Take pain relief, a subject which was discussed in the previous chapter. If you have a dull ache, imagine placing a warm bottle against it. Some pain reacts better to coolness than to warmth, so the image of ice packs might work well. Should the pain be sharp, turn it into some other sensation, such as a vibration. Or you might think of it as a rigid block of ice which slowly melts away and dissolves. This image may be useful if the pain covers a wide area. Warmth can also help in this situation, so imagine yourself in a soothing spa bath.

If the pain is of the stabbing variety, imagine the affected body part to be very soft and yielding like a feather pillow. This absorbs the stabbing impact without feeling it. Should the pain be burning, imagine applying a soothing liquid, cool and comfortable. Such imagery is not difficult to achieve because it makes use of everyday objects with which we are familiar.

To handle *backache*, you might like to imagine a softly

glowing light bulb being placed first below, then above, and then directly on, the painful spot. This bulb, which radiates a pleasant and gentle warmth, may be used to ease the whole spine. Take it slowly, letting the warmth soak into the affected areas gently and easily.

If *nausea* is the problem imagine that you are inhaling coolness into the upper part of your body. As you exhale, imagine your breath leaving through a hole in the small of your back, or through the big toe, relaxing your lower body as it does so.

Relaxation is best achieved during exhalation of breath, and most ailments improve when we get rid of tension. So it is often useful to link images and breathing — a point which is continually stressed by Jencks in *Respiration for Relaxation, Invigoration and Special Accomplishments*. When speaking of *arthritis,* Jencks suggests that pains may be eased by imagining, as you exhale, a warm shower over the shoulders and neck, or a warm blanket over the knees. Cupping the affected area with a warm hand is likely to increase the effect, as does imagining the area becoming loose, soft and warm during exhalations.

We tend to relax as we breathe out, and so we are likely to become more flexible at such times. Arthritis sufferers might like to imagine as they exhale that their hip, knee, and ankle joints are flexible rubber. Another method to loosen the joints is to imagine putting a drop of oil into each, then to either actually move the joint or to imagine moving it during exhalation. It is possible to feel the oil distributing itself as it eases movement.

Another way of using an image to relieve arthritis is to visualize a calcium deposit between your bones, and to suggest to yourself that in future a drop of lubrication will be secreted each time you move the affected arm or leg. Each minute drop of secretion will tend to cover the calcium deposit, removing friction and discomfort. Arthritics are not the only persons who can benefit from such images. Athletes, stiff after sport, also find them useful, as do typists who have spent a long day at the keyboard.

Similar principles, involving the matching of simple images and breathing, can also help with *eye* problems. Close your eyes. How do they feel? Tense? Dry? Burning? Is there movement? Consider the hollows surrounding the eyes. Do your eyes feel comfortable and easy in their sockets? Your answers to such questions will provide a guide to what sort of help is needed. If tension is noticeable, think of the eyes 'letting go' as you breathe out. With each exhalation, they become increasingly loose, as you imagine a comfortable heaviness in your eyelids.

Should dryness be the problem, think of your eyeballs swimming in a warm bath, caressed by the liquid. If movement of your eyes is disturbing you, imagine the activity melting away with each out-breath, thinking 'calm' and 'still' as you do. For burning eyes, visualize them floating in cool, soothing water.

The same idea of using warming or cooling images can apply to many of our ailments. For a running *nose,* imagine drawing in cool dry air; and if your nose is stuffy or dry, visualize breathing in warm, moist air. Though the concept is a very simple one, it can produce benefits out of all proportion to its simplicity.

Relieving the discomfort of tinnitis

It is not pleasant to hear ringing in the ears. Gloria Anthony did, very frequently. Often, while at the school where she worked as a teacher, or at home, she was conscious of the ringing sound in her ears. When she came to consult me about her problem she was quite distraught.

We began with some relaxation training. After some initial difficulties (Gloria insisted that she could not possibly relax) she was able to let go quite well. Many people are like Gloria in this. They use the label 'I can't' for many things. If they keep telling themselves that they cannot, well, obviously, this is true. However, substitution of 'I won't' for 'I can't' often produces interesting changes. It certainly did for Gloria. In the relaxed state, she tuned in to her ringing sound, linking it to a control knob which she had created as a mental image. By using this knob she was able to turn the sound up or down. That is, she could then take control of it instead of allowing it to control her.

Gloria also linked her sound to the positive feeling of enjoyment which she derived from her relaxation experience. Whenever she became aware of the ringing in her ears, she now treated it as a cue to remember that feeling and to realize that she could control its volume at will.

The meaning of the sound changed even further when Gloria realized its value as an early warning signal of distress. Whenever things mounted up on her or whenever she perceived any threats and demands in her environment, Gloria heard the ringing in her ears. When relaxed, she was not conscious of it. However, she had not previously realized this connection. Once she had done so, she welcomed the sound as a friendly warning to slow down, relax, turn off the distress. And as she did so, the ringing would disappear.

As a result of changing the meaning of the sound, Gloria came to see it as positive and not negative. Instead of keeping her control knob as a means of regulating its intensity, she now linked it to her distress level. Whenever she would receive her early warning signal, she would turn down her arousal level, reducing her agitation both through the use of the control knob and through other imaginative calming techniques.

Handling headaches and migraine

The control knob idea can be of use in relieving headaches, too, as the discomfort is turned down. Another simple way of handling this problem is to go inside your head and picture the ache. Imagine yourself putting water on it. If this does not work, put a special chemical on it. Perhaps you can see your head as a large cube of ice. As the ice melts, so does your ache. It gradually flows away as the ice changes to water. You may like to use the black velvet curtain which I mentioned in the second chapter. See that curtain in your mind, soft and gentle. As you watch it, all discomfort, all tension, all strain just melt away, effortlessly, peacefully, allowing you to rest in comfort. If all else fails, which is rarely the case, it may be necessary to imagine digging a ditch around your headache so that at least it will not spread.

Instead of the simple images so far described, you may prefer a more involved fantasy. A pleasant one is used by an ex-patient of mine, Alex Masters. Alex imagines himself as a dolphin, swimming along lazily just below the surface of the sea. He feels the warm water on his back and the cooler water beneath him. As he visualizes himself diving to the sea floor, he is aware of increased coldness and pressure. He adapts quite easily to these, as his headache fades away in the face of the cool, soothing currents which flow over him. Alex imagines himself drifting ever downward, past seaweed forests and deep coral canyons, until he reaches the sea floor. This he explores, savouring the cool freshness and tranquility of the deep. On his return to the surface, which is very leisurely, Alex enjoys freedom from any head discomfort.

Fantasies involving coolness of the head are particularly appropriate for migraine sufferers, particularly when linked to a warming of the right hand. This may be done by imagining yourself warming it in front of a fire or radiator, or immersing it in hot water, or feeling the sun's rays raising its temperature. Couple this lift in the temperature of the right hand with a cooling of the forehead. This is often more difficult to achieve than a warm hand and, although it can make it easier to 'turn off' a migraine, it is fortunately not essential.

The theory behind such imagery is that it draws blood

from the head into your hand. Obviously, if you are near a water supply, the easiest thing to do is to immerse your hand in hot water and place a cold towel on your forehead. However, if no water is available, your imagination can prove to be a very effective substitute. You can go into additional detail if you so desire. Visualize your head gradually becoming transparent so that you can see through the skin and bone to your brain. There you can see the blood vessels, which provide circulation and nourishment, rolling along the brain's surface.

Your imagery from this point depends on your experience with your migraine. If, in the past, it has tended to feel better with a cold pack, then imagine the blood vessels becoming smaller so that the blood flow is reduced. Should a hot water bottle have been more useful previously, then visualize the blood vessels becoming larger during the migraine. Gradually let the blood vessels return to normal, retaining either the comfortable feeling of warmth or coolness.

For such visualizations, recourse to a medical book showing the brain and its blood vessels would be of value. It is helpful, too, to take action at the first faint signs that a migraine is beginning. Though it is often relatively easy for many people to 'turn off' a migraine before it takes hold, it is far more difficult to do anything about it once it has started.

Should you suffer from migraine, it might be worth having a hard look at yourself and your attitudes. Many migraine sufferers have a strong perfectionist streak, together with equally strong guilt feelings about idleness and imperfection. This has a positive aspect in that such people strive to attain the highest standards. Unfortunately, however, when perfection is established as a goal, they will always fail, because human beings simply are not perfect. This is the negative aspect, the sense of guilt over the failure to reach the impossibly high standards.

In addition, migraine sufferers are frequently slaves to the clock. This shows up in the development of migraine attacks in 'let down' periods, such as the night-time, weekends, and holidays. Migraine suferers tend to push themselves, often turning hobbies and recreations into hard work. They build up high tension levels, then 'crash' with the migraine when they are taking a break from intense activity. Though not all people who experience migraines have such personality characteristics, many do. So, if you recognize yourself in the description, it might be as well to examine your belief system and your values. Are migraines too high a price to pay for your attempts to attain perfection?

There are different kinds of perfection, of course. Whereas the migraine sufferer will often strive to do virtually everything perfectly, others direct their efforts towards physical perfection. Cosmetic surgery, body building, diet and exercise are all used to help in the attainment of such a goal. Imagination might be of assistance, too.

Changing body shape

Probably *weight loss* is the best example. It is possible to lose weight through visualizing yourself as you want to be. By doing this at times when you are relaxed, particularly as you drift off to sleep at night, you have an excellent chance of convincing your unconscious mind that you are actually like this. Imagine yourself stripping away the unwanted weight from the body and 'dumping' it down a chute or burning it away to nothing on a fire, and then getting on a set of scales which show your weight to be as you want it to be.

At times when you are relaxing, see yourself in this way and let images float through your mind. Every time you are tempted to overeat, visualize yourself on the scales, or see your desired weight flashing in your mind like a neon sign. To stimulate your imagination, find pictures of yourself when you were your desired weight. Put them all around the house so that you see them frequently. Hang clothes which you like, but which are now too tight, in your bedroom where you can see them frequently. Imagine yourself wearing these clothes and looking the way you want to look. Visualize yourself eating small meals, leaving food on the plate and rejecting high-calorie, unhealthy foods in favour of low-calorie healthy foods.

Imagine yourself entering a 'special room' where food does not exist. You will be able to remember this room whenever you are in danger of eating either too much or eating at the wrong time. You might like to make use of a control knob again, picturing it in one part of the room. When turned on, it creates hunger within you; when turned off, it removes all sense of hunger. Perhaps, in the door to this room, you could place a dial which enables you to dial your desired weight. Inside could be banks of light bathing the centre of the room in a warm glow. As you stand in this warm glow you can see and feel the weight being drawn off from your body.

Project yourself into the future. Imagine yourself three months on from the present time, when weight has been lost and you are looking so much better. You are wearing the clothes that you want to wear, you are exercising more because you enjoy doing so, and you are feeling a sense of pride in yourself for taking more control over your weight.

Naturally enough, the same methods may be used to *gain weight*. Just as it is possible to imagine yourself becoming slimmer, shedding surplus weight from some parts of the body rather than others, so you can imagine adding weight to either the body as a whole or to certain selected body parts. In particular, some research in the late 1970s suggests that the imagination might be used to encourage *breast enlargement*.

An important aspect of this approach is time distortion, which has been described in some detail in the fifth chapter. Should you want to make use of this method, induce a trance state and go back in time to an age somewhere when you were between 10 and 12 years old. Place your hands on your breasts. Imagine growth sensations such as swelling, tightness of skin, slight tenderness, and imagine that your hands are being gently pushed upward as your breasts grow larger.

This age regression is linked to age progression. Imagine yourself at a time two or three years into the future. You have just finished showering and are standing nude in front of the bathroom mirror. As you inspect your appearance, you are very pleased at the sight of the larger, more attractive breasts which have resulted from your treatment.

The procedure already described might be strengthened by visualizing (or actually placing) a warm, wet towel over your breasts. If it is difficult to obtain a feeling of warmth, add the visualization of a heat lamp shining on the warm towel. Once you can experience the warmth, concentrate on a feeling of pulsation in the breasts. Become aware of your heartbeat, and allow it to flow into your breasts. During the day, create a spontaneous feeling of warmth and pulsation by using your imagination in this way. Constant practice is essential if any change is to be effected.

Controlling breathing and circulation

Age regression may be helpful, too, if *asthma* is a problem. Allowing yourself to drift back to the time of your first attack could enable you to identify whatever it was that provided the trigger. As an adult you can see this event from a different perspective, realizing that though it may have been frightening or upsetting to a child, now it need no longer be so. Therefore, it is now possible to let go of the fears and tensions about the need to breathe and let it happen naturally. You might like to mentally remake this early situation so that the elements stimulating fear and tension are removed and a different positive outcome eventuates. Imagine this several times.

Most imaginative approaches to helping asthma sufferers involve visualizations relating to the breathing apparatus as, during attacks, the airways to the lungs become narrower. These airways or tubes may be seen as opening wider and wider as the chest relaxes and breathing becomes slower. Or perhaps colour might be used. What colour are your lungs today? What colour is the air today? Should the lungs be, say, blue and the air yellow, you can imagine taking a deep breath, watching the yellow air go all the way down to the very bottom of your lungs. At this time, all you see is yellow. Then breathe out, watching the yellow air come up so that, from top to bottom, your lungs are again blue.

Thinking of a situation in which you would feel comfortable can be useful. Asthma sufferers frequently use images of mountains. Here they are breathing clean, pure, sparkling air that creates a spirit of vitality and joy. Should you feel an attack coming on, imagine this situation, perhaps recalling the fragrant scent of pine trees as you inhale cool mountain air.

Just as you can exert some control over your breathing, so you can influence your blood circulation. This is apparent in the migraine treatment when you warmed your hand and directed an increased blood flow to it. It is also a way to overcoming *blushing*, an apparently involuntary process which can be a source of great embarrassment. Imagine yourself in a shower, becoming quite hot. After several minutes, visualize yourself lying in a cool bath with a comfortably cold flannel over your face.

Alternate the hot shower and the cool bath until you feel that you have developed control over your skin temperature, being able to raise and lower it as you imagine the appropriate image. Also, use other images of heat, such as being in a sauna or lying in the sun, and of cold, such as being in an ice house or a swimming pool. With this control, you can imagine cold whenever you feel yourself blushing. This will normally solve the problem. Similarly, imagine hot whenever you feel uncomfortably chilled.

Blood pressure can be influenced also through your imagination. Visualize the blood vessels in your body leading into a pump that represents your heart. The blood vessels that you see at first are extremely narrow and very tight. The pump is working unusually hard to get the blood through them, and its pressure gauge is very high, in the red danger zone. You direct your mind to relax the tight blood vessels. See them open up immediately. They increase noticeably in size, the blood courses through them, and the pressure gauge drops from the danger zone into the safe green area.

As we are able to exert some control over our blood circulation and pressure, it is also possible to influence *bleeding*. This might be done by visualizing the blood flowing out from a wound as if it is water from a tap. This you can turn off. Or you might imagine that you are stitching the wound so that it will bleed no more. Going further, it is possible to actually constrict the blood vessels in the area so that blood flow is reduced. Images of coldness are likely to be helpful in this situation, as they are with skin troubles too.

Skin problems

Imagining yourself immersed in water has proven effective on many occasions, particularly for easing the discomfort of itching skin. Visualize yourself beside a lake. Take a deep breath, filling your lungs with fresh air. Feel the warmth of the sun on your face. Listen to the sighing of the breeze through the nearby trees. Walk into the water. Enjoy the coolness, first around your ankles and legs, then around your body as you submerge. The cool water soothes your skin, smoothing and healing it as all irritation disappears.

You may also soothe, purify, and cleanse your skin by spraying on a shimmering sunlit liquid with special healing properties, or by imagining that you are enveloped in a layer of cotton wool which acts as a protective coating.

Of all skin problems, perhaps warts are most amenable to treatment through imagination. Usually, imagery related to controlling the blood supply is the most effective. Rob Garrett, the young son of a colleague of mine, visualizes a pump with an on-off switch and tubes leading from the pump to the wart. In the off position, the pump cuts off the blood supply to the wart which turns brown, shrivels up and falls off.

Rob has used this method quite successfully to rid himself of a number of warts. With any that are particularly stubborn, he uses a special lotion which he dabs on. He enhances the effect of this by imagining it penetrating the wart and killing the cells inside it, so that it dries up and drops away. This use of the imagination to increase the power of conventional treatment is very valuable, not only in terms of speeding up healing but also for the feeling of being able to do something positive about a problem.

Bed-wetting and the imagination

Being able to take an active part in healing engenders a feeling of self-confidence. Rob, for instance, tackles the healing of his warts quite confidently because of his earlier success in coping with the problem of bed-wetting. He used the split screen technique as described in Chapter 8, seeing himself on the right-hand segment of the screen as he woke in the morning with a wet bed. Then, as he wiped this image away, he saw himself on the centre segment taking a homoeopathic remedy called 'Equisetum'. Finally, he let go of this image and saw himself on the left-hand segment waking with a dry bed.

Rob also used the imagery of a dam with sluice gates holding back the flow of water. When these gates were open, water was able to pass through the dam; when they were closed, no water was able to pass. He had quite an elaborate, computer-controlled instrument panel to regulate the movement of the gates. Just before going to bed, Rob would ensure that they were closed. When he awoke in the morning, he would open them. In this way, he overcame his bed-wetting habit and enjoyed an uninterrupted night's sleep. This is a much sought after outcome, not limited only to bed-wetters.

And so to sleep

Your imagination can be a potent ally in helping you overcome *insomnia*. Focus your mind on total empty blackness until you can make a single disc of black come out of it. Keep your mind's eye on this black disc until you fall asleep. Or return to the blackboard of earlier chapters. Imagine yourself at a blackboard with a piece of chalk and an eraser. Draw a circle, then write inside it the number 100. Erase this number slowly, using your eraser in an anti-clockwise circular motion. Once you have done so, write the words 'deep sleep' to one side of the circle. Now, put the number 99 in the circle, erase it, and write carefully over the words 'deep sleep' again, ensuring that there are no double lines. Continue until you fall asleep. If you should wake in the night, keep going where you left off, or start again.

Alternatively, you might like to become aware of the point at which the back of your head comes into maximum contact with the bed. After dwelling on this for 20 to 30 seconds, imagine that you are looking at something that is very far away from you. Do this for 20 to 30 seconds, then imagine a faint breeze moving across your right cheek. After about half a minute, become aware of how close your breath comes to the back of your eyes each time you inhale. After a further 20 to 30 seconds, feel heaviness coming into your legs. By this time you are probably asleep; but, if not, keep recycling through the five concentration points.

Perhaps you would prefer to use sounds. Become aware of the most distant sounds that you can hear. Search them out, follow each for a few seconds, shifting your attention from sound to sound without attempting to identify the source. Gradually focus on closer sounds. Develop an awareness of your room, so that you visualize, with eyes closed, the four walls, ceiling, floor, your body lying on the bed in perfect stillness. Feel the meeting points between your body and the bed, then flow with your breathing.

Carry this further. Step out of yourself, and sit down in a comfortable chair beside the bed. Notice your other self, on the bed, breathing more slowly, more deeply, and more rhythmically. See the slow, rhythmic rise and fall of the chest, the calm, relaxed expression on the face. As you continue to look at this image of yourself, you will become increasingly relaxed, increasingly drowsy. You see the image on the bed drifting effortlessly into sleep as you rise from the chair, re-enter, and become as one with your real self.

You might prefer to indulge yourself with a tropical island fantasy. There you are, standing beside a jungle pool fed by a waterfall. The water is clear and inviting, so you slide into the comfortably warm pool. Feel the warmth moving up your body as you wade in further. First your feet, calves, and thighs experience the gentle warmth, then your body, arms, and neck as you immerse yourself completely. Swim towards the waterfall. There you find a large, flat rock that you can stand upon. As you do so, you can feel the warm water from the waterfall cascading over your body, massaging and soothing it. Any worries, tensions, and problems are washed away, leaving a feeling of absolute serenity.

Enjoy this feeling. Every muscle, nerve and fibre in your body is at peace, still and calm. Step out from under the waterfall. Stretch out on the smooth sun-warmed rock. The fresh air and sunshine, the warm rock beneath you, the soft jungle sounds in the distance, all create an atmosphere so tranquil that you feel drowsy, comfortable. Sleep. It is so good to sleep, to overcome the insomnia habit. Life becomes more enjoyable, just as it does when we overcome other habits which are negative in nature.

Habits best banished

Smoking is one habit which is very likely to interfere with our lives in a negative way. It kills us. Or if it does not kill us, it is certainly likely to have a bad effect on our general health. You may be able to transform your enjoyment of cigarettes into a powerful dislike. Singer and Switzer in *Mind Play* suggest that the following imagery may help you do so:

- Imagine the cigarette smoke being drawn down into your lungs, corroding them until they are a mass of raw flesh, black pus, and dead tissue.
- Imagine your cigarette as a filthy stick which you picked up on the road. It is covered with worms and slime so that, as you put it into your mouth, you gag over it.
- You are in a hot, airless room, filled with clouds of thick, corrosive smoke. Breathing is difficult. You gasp for air. You struggle to open the window but cannot do so. Nor can you open the door. You're stuck, having to stay in that room, breathing in the noxious fumes until your head spins and you feel sick.

This type of aversive imagery can be used as a weapon against the overuse of *alcohol* too. Imagine that someone has vomited all over your beer glass. Make this scene as revolting as possible. Then imagine that you have to drink this beer, tasting the slimy vile vomit in your mouth.

Rather than imagine yourself in such situations, you may find it more effective to visualize someone else in them, with yourself as an unwilling spectator. See someone whom you like very much reaching for a cigarette. As he or she lights it, a violent electric shock races through the body, causing a look of intense agony on the face. Every time this person touches a cigarette, you see him or her writhing in pain.

This aversive, unpleasant imagery might be necessary to counter dangerous habits, though I personally prefer the more positive approach of earlier chapters. Whatever imagery is used, we need to have confidence that we can accomplish the changes we want in ourselves through the use of our imagination. However, we can, in fact, also use our imagination as a way of increasing our self-confidence generally. We will look into how this might be accomplished in the next chapter.

11 Increasing Self-Confidence

Confidence building through the pyramid

A powerful way of creating increased self-confidence is through the use of symbols. One of these, the tree, was described earlier in Chapter 2. Another is the pyramid, a fantasy described by Gibbons in his book *Beyond Hypnosis*. I have found this fantasy to be of great value in unlocking previously unused inner potentials.

Begin by visualizing yourself in ancient Egypt, standing in the desert before the cave-like entrance to a large pyramid which towers above you, its top lost to view in the darkness of a desert sandstorm. Perhaps, as well as seeing this scene, you may be able to hear the wind whistling in your ears and feel the driven sand stinging your cheeks.

You enter the pyramid, finding yourself in a passageway well lit by torches fastened to the wall at regular intervals. As you follow along this passageway it slopes downward. Feeling quite safe and secure, you go deeper and deeper into the heart of the pyramid. What you are really doing is going deeper into your own mind as you follow the passage down, down, down.

At the very end of the passage, you come upon a vast storehouse filled with treasures of all descriptions. This is the storehouse of all the vast untapped resources within you. Herein lies all the potential for good and for achievement which you have not yet turned to your advantage. All of this treasure is rightfully yours, for it has been stolen from you through force of circumstance. Unless you carry it back into the world outside to enjoy and to share with others it will eventually be sealed up within the room and lost forever.

You attempt to gather up some of the treasure. You cannot. Something stops you. Suddenly your gaze is drawn to one particular jewel, more brilliant than all the rest. It is embedded in the forehead of a huge, forbidding statue in the centre of the room. This statue, powered by the jewel in its forehead, is the embodiment of all the negative forces of failure and defeat which are within the personality of each one who looks at it. It has been placed in the room as a guardian of the treasure, making all other guardians unnecessary.

In order to free this vast storehouse of your potential, so that you can become the person you are capable of being, you have first to overcome the negative tendencies within you which are acting to prevent this, as personified and embodied in the statue before you. On the wall is an ornamental dagger. Seizing it, you spring upon the statue, striking the jewel from its forehead in one quick blow. As it rests upon the ground, you see that the jewel no longer glows, but lies dark and ugly before you like a lump of coal. You can grind it to black dust under your feet, then push the statue so it falls and breaks into many pieces. Its power is gone.

You are now free to gather up as much of the treasure as you can, carrying it with you as you retrace your steps up the passage to the entrance. As you step outside, you find that the sandstorm has gone. The sky is blue, the sun is shining and you can see for miles in every direction. You walk cheerfully away from the pyramid, knowing that your return to the world of your everyday life will allow these treasures to show themselves in new habits, new ideas, and new directions which will enhance your life. Each time you return to the pyramid you will be able to recover more treasure from the storehouse of your potential, and, no matter how much treasure you may gather, the storehouse will never be empty.

This fantasy can build confidence in two ways. Firstly, it will help you feel that you can draw much more effectively on your inner resources and strengths than you have ever done before. Secondly, you can use the pyramid as a confidence symbol. On occasions when you doubt your ability to achieve something, when you are inclined to think 'I can't', visualize the pyramid. As you do, feel a sense of power flowing within you, a belief in yourself and your capabilities. This confidence can also be engendered with many other images and symbols.

Confidence-building imagery

Imagine yourself on a shore of a lake. The water is rough, whipped up by wind and rain. It is a dreary, depressing scene. In the distance you see the other shore of the lake. There all is brightness. It is bathed in sunshine, with relaxed people working and playing. This is the shore of normality and health.

Visualize yourself crossing the lake in some way that requires effort on your part. Swimming or rowing would be two possibilities. Perhaps there are obstacles which impede your progress, but you either overcome or swim around these. If the distance seems too great, make use of small islands which dot the surface of the lake. These will provide you with an opportunity to rest. When you do reach the bright shore, feel a surge of belief in your ability to live your life as you want to, coping effectively and happily with whatever your environment provides. As with the pyramid, you may wish to use the bright shore of the lake as an image which symbolizes your feelings of confidence. Thus, when faced with any future problem situation, recall the symbol and re-experience these feelings.

A rather different image would have you visualize yourself sitting in a room on one end of a couch. Imagine seeing your 'ideal self' walk into the room and sit down at the other end of the couch. Mentally describe this 'ideal self' of yours in some detail, both in terms of appearance and behaviour. See yourself moving slowly on the couch, coming closer and closer to your 'ideal self'. Finally, actually merge into this other body until only one of you remains. Now, act as if you and your 'ideal self' are identical, completely fused. You will strengthen your confidence using such an image.

Another image which is designed to serve the same purpose is to imagine yourself standing at the top of a large, snow-covered mountain looking down into the valley below. In this valley, at the foot of the mountain, is your destination; but, before you can reach it, you have to overcome all sorts of barriers and obstacles. These are the symbols of the things which have, in your life, prevented you from obtaining your goals.

Bend down, pick up a handful of snow, and examine it. Notice how soft and powdery it is — something like your own confidence, which lacks strength. See yourself packing the snow together in your hand, compressing it into a snowball. Add more snow. Pack it down into a firm, hard, round ball. As you do, feel your own confidence, courage, and resolution becoming stronger and firmer too.

Walk over to a very steep incline at the side of the mountain. Start the snowball on its journey, rolling it straight at the obstacles which lie between you and your destination. Slowly the snowball gathers pace, picking up more and more snow, becoming bigger and bigger. Soon it is boulder size, huge and powerful. Now it is a veritable avalanche, sweeping everything before it as it continues on its way to the bottom of the mountain.

The way is clear before you now. All obstacles have been swept away. You can stride down the mountain, knowing that, as you do, your self-confidence, courage and resolve grow stronger and stronger, as did the snowball. You, too, will be able to sweep aside obstacles, overcome barriers, and attain the goals in life which you have set yourself. When you doubt this, imagine the snowball growing in power to vanquish everything blocking its path, and you will feel your self-confidence renewed.

Overcoming barriers and obstacles is important if we are to become all that we are capable of being. The snowball is a useful mental image to help you achieve this. You will find other images in the next section.

Overcoming obstacles

A student whom I helped some years ago — I will call her Liza Maddell — learned to use a number of barrier-smashing images. These have helped her feel much greater confidence in her ability to achieve previously unattainable goals. She visualizes, for example, a particular barrier as a brick wall. At the base of this wall, she plants demolition charges. Moving back to safety, Liza detonates these, blowing the wall apart. She is then able to confidently move past the now non-existent barrier.

On other occasions, when negative ideas from the past or suggestions of limitation occupy her mind, Liza symbolizes them as a piece of thick glass placed between herself and the world. To achieve full appreciation and knowledge of the world, Liza uses a long-handled sledgehammer to smash the glass. Thus, she destroys the obstacles or the limitations, which are undermining her confidence.

A third technique which Liza uses is to imagine herself becoming smaller and smaller until she is able to enter into her own body. She then travels to the control room of her mind to repair the 'mental block', whatever it might be. Liza remembers this control room whenever she feels blocked, particularly during examinations.

A final image in Liza's repertoire has her visualizing her outstretched wrists being held close together by a large rubber band. This rubber band represents all the negative thoughts and feelings which are undermining her confidence. She sees her hands and arms becoming increasingly powerful so that they draw further and further apart, stretching the band until it suddenly snaps, ridding her of the confidence-sapping influences. Again, she employs the image of the rubber band snapping to engender a confident and positive frame of mind if self-doubt should assail her. Because of this use of her imagination, Liza is able to assert herself more effectively.

Asserting yourself

Being able to assert yourself to gain whatever it is that you want is very much a function of your self-confidence. Anything that you can do to increase your ability to assert yourself is also likely to increase your confidence. The usual way of using your imagination to improve your assertive skills is to imagine a series of scenarios. In these, you act assertively (without being aggressive or hostile) to achieve your objective.

If you should be having some difficulty in telling an employee that he has made a mistake, you might set up a scene depicting that situation. Often, visualizing the scene taking place on a screen or on a stage with you looking on can be quite effective. See yourself handling the situation calmly and quietly, but achieving what you want so that the employee remedies his mistake.

Perhaps, you are constantly being overwhelmed by a husband, wife, mother, or mother-in-law. This person imposes his or her will on you. You seethe inwardly but do not seem able to assert your right to behave in the way which you think appropriate. In other words, you lack self-confidence.

So, play a typical scene over in your mind, first as it usually happens. Then wipe this away and replay it as you want it to happen, with you asserting yourself effectively. Make sure that your scene finishes with an outcome which is beneficial to you. This visualization of success is vital.

Modelling is just as useful here — as indeed it is in the other situations described in this book. Think of someone you admire; someone who is able to get what he or she wants without bulldozing other people and depriving them of their rights; someone who quietly and consistently asserts his or her right to be heard, express opinions, and behave constructively to achieve goals. Really throw yourself into the personality of that model. Try to think as the model, to talk in the same way, to emulate his or her behaviour. In other words, act as if you were that person. Imagine yourself in your new role, behaving assertively.

Practice a variety of scenarios. Imagine how your model would handle a situation in which he or she had to go out later in the evening for an important appointment. Friends drop in. They show no sign of leaving. Visualize your model behaving in a way which gives the results he or she wants, but without offending the friends. Perhaps the model says something like: 'I've really enjoyed you dropping in, and I feel quite disappointed that I have to go out. I hope we can get together some other time when we are all free.'

Once you have the scene running to your satisfaction, become your model. The essence is to get what you want without making life difficult for others. Sometimes, this is not easy and you have to live with the fact that your assertive action might upset someone else. While seeing a film, for example, you may be sitting in front of several people who are talking incessantly, interfering with your desire to hear what is happening. First, see your model turning to say: 'Would you mind stopping talking please so that I can enjoy the film?' Then see yourself doing it. It is really amazing how many people will put up with the poor behaviour of others because they are unwilling or unable to assert themselves.

Actually, I believe that the best way of training yourself to become more confident in asserting yourself is to remake each day. At night, go back over your day, praising yourself for the occasions on which you did assert yourself. Then, one at a time, take each situation when you did not do so. See it in your mind, wipe it away, and replay it as you would have preferred to behave. If done in a trance state or just before you drop off to sleep, the procedure becomes even more effective. This point has been made elsewhere in this book, but the technique is so valuable that it bears repetition. It can be useful in so many situations, including that of the deliberate changing of mood states.

Changing your mood

This is not the only way to achieve such a change. The first step to take, when immersed in a bad mood which you would like to change, is to relax, at least a little. Then engage in some thought switching. Draw out a jewel of a memory from the 'jewel box' in your mind. Linger on it. Vividly recreate the pleasant sensations which made it so important to you. Perhaps humour was involved. Humour is a marvellous way to dissolve unhappiness. Remember funny scenes from your life, or films and TV shows at which you have laughed.

Obviously, changing imagery to change your mood cannot solve the problem which has sparked off your unhappiness. It can, however, break you out of the depressed, self-defeating frame of mind which often leads to foolish, unconsidered actions — such as breaking off a relationship, resigning from a job, getting drunk or hitting your children. We may deeply regret such actions later. We do these things while in a black mood, and it is quite likely that we would never have done them if we had set about changing our mood state.

Not that it is easy. Often it isn't. It takes an act of will to get started, but it is well worth the effort. We gain increased confidence in our ability to control our lives each time we successfully transform a black mood into a sunny one. Start before you are in the bad mood. Make a list of your pleasures and delights, the memories you relish. Choose one that is particularly vivid for you. And then, as Jean Houston puts it in *The Possible Human:*

> Visualize the experience as strongly as possible, hear it, taste it, smell it, let it fill your entire body. Experience it down your spine, breathe into it, laugh into it, smile into it. Reach out and hug it. Hold it to you and then let it go.

Now, you have this memory and others as well, which you can use when you are dwelling on miserable thoughts. Think of the pleasant memory before going into a situation that you expect to be difficult. Keep it in mind during the situation. Or, alternatively, stop every so often during the day and simply experience the moment. Focus on the sense of being alive, of the pleasure of being well fed, well clothed, of the enjoyment of your family and friends. By reminding ourselves of how much pleasure and beauty there is around us, we build up resources to combat miserable moods.

Make a list of objects associated with your father or your mother, such as the things that they wore or used. Concentrate on each object, picturing yourself wearing, holding or touching the object. Select the one which has the most positive influence on you, using this image as a trigger for changing your emotional state.

Or use a mental blackboard technique similar to the one described in Chapter 5. Divide the blackboard into two halves with a vertical line. On the left-hand side write, in small letters, an undesired feeling such as 'unhappiness'. Erase it. On the right-hand side, at the top, write in large letters a desired feeling such as 'happiness'. Leave it there. You may want to continue the same procedure for other desired and undesired feelings. When you have finished, go over the left-hand side of the blackboard with a wet cloth, wiping it very clean. While it is drying, underline each desirable feeling which is listed on the right-hand side. By doing this, you encourage your unconscious mind to wipe out the undesired feeling, replacing it with the one you desire. This sort of mood alteration can also be seen in the wider context of attitude change.

Coping with the fear of death

Fear undermines self-confidence. Nowhere is this more apparent than in the fear of death. To be able to live meaningfully, it has been suggested, we must first learn to die. This can be done through using our imagination to provide a substitute for the actual experience of dying. Not only does death imagery provide an opportunity for confronting death, but it may also lead to increased self-awareness and to the resolving of internal conflicts, as well as a sense of belief in one's ability to handle a previously fear-provoking situation.

Relaxation is the way in to such imagery. In fact, it has been suggested that death is the ultimate relaxation. People who have used death imagery often report that dying in imagination turns out to be a deeply relaxing experience. Perhaps this may be due to a feeling that the burden and weight of living is lifted, that there is really nothing to fear in letting go of life.

Be that as it may, once you are relaxed, possibly through deep breathing or some other trance-induction method, spend a few moments imagining that you are faced with death, that you are going to die and that there is nothing you can do about it. Then, think of all the people with whom you have some emotional bond. This may be positive or it may be negative. Imagine yourself interacting with each of these people in turn, resolving any unfinished business from the past. Make peace with them. Take your leave of them.

Surprisingly enough, many people who have used death imagery report that saying goodbye to loved ones is quite painless in that the feelings they experience are usually very positive. This is captured well in the case of Christine, described by Sheikh in the book *The Potential of Fantasy and Imagination.* Christine reported part of her experience in these words:

> My body became lighter and lighter until I began to float up and away from my body. Suddenly, with one deep breath, I was adrift in a quiet world of blue-white light . . . As I floated, I first had the shape of a ball, warm and alive. But as I soared through the windless space, I separated into a billion particles, mixing with the light and energy, and experiencing an exhilaration at being able to do so. I crossed vast expanses of space, infused with a feeling of being part of the light. Time became meaningless. The sound of the world around me . . . all became muted and distant. Peace and serenity flooded my being.

After her experience, Christine's attitude to death changed considerably, the greatest gain being an increased sense of confidence in living positively and fully. Many other people, too, have perhaps somewhat paradoxically, experienced a rebirth of self-confidence through experiencing their deaths in imagination. By so doing they have enriched their lives. Let us look now at other avenues leading to life-enrichment.

12 Life Enrichment

Improving your study skills

Life is a learning experience. Some of us, however, learn more formally than others. This involves study. It also involves examinations designed to indicate whether we have actually learned or not. Though gaining new knowledge can certainly enrich our lives, sometimes the difficulty of studying and the tension of examinations provides too big a hurdle. We drop out. Yet, there are simple ways of using our imagination which will enable us to cope more effectively with the challenge of study.

The mental rehearsal technique, which has already been described in reference to other problems, remains one of the best. When you imagine yourself, or an admired model, studying and sitting for examinations successfully, you condition your unconscious mind in a very positive way.

The magic circle technique does this too. Induce a relaxed state, and imagine yourself in the place where you normally study. Visualize yourself concentrating really well, giving your undivided attention to the task at hand. See yourself placing together the thumb and forefinger of each of your hands. As you visualize this, actually do it. Suggest to yourself that, in future, should you have any difficulty studying, then all you will need to do is place together the thumb and forefinger of each hand. The circle you create will always work its magic, establishing for you both the necessary concentration and the desire to study.

You can use exactly the same technique for coping with examinations. Visualize yourself handling the examination really well, linking the magic circle to that success. When actually sitting for an examination, you will be able to recreate the success experience by the joining of thumb and forefinger. Should you have difficulty in recalling a specific item of information heard in class or read during study time, the magic circle technique is likely to help you remember what you need to know.

Good concentration is an essential element of successful study. Liza Maddell, the student to whom I referred in the last chapter, has greatly improved her ability to concentrate through use of the following exercise. Once she has relaxed, Liza imagines a large black curtain. On this she pins, one at a time, the numbers 1 to 20. She visualizes her hands with a large, golden 1 in them, and she sees these hands pinning the number on the black curtain. The number is left there until it has remained in clear detail and bright colour for at least five seconds. Then, Liza imagines her hands removing the number and replacing it with a 2. It takes practice to keep the numbers sharply focused, but Liza feels that the effort is worthwhile. Her visualization abilities have improved noticeably and it has become increasingly easy for her to devote her undivided attention to whatever she is studying.

She has also used her imagination to improve her memory, employing an ancient technique which dates from the time of Cicero, the Roman senator. If she has a sequence of facts to remember, Liza places them in a number of familiar locations. Fact one would be associated with her bed. Fact two would 'sit' on the chair from which she picks up her dressing gown each morning. The dressing gown would be her link to fact three, while the bedroom door would contain fact four. And so on. Because of the familiar routine followed each morning (leaving her bed, going to the chair, putting on her dressing gown, and opening the door), Liza has provided four slots in a mental filing system. She can add as many more as she likes by continuing the sequence as she goes into the passage, enters the kitchen, picks up a glass, and so on. Each familiar place or object provides one more slot.

This is a rather mechanical process, but one that is very useful for remembering a sequence of items, such as points to be made in a speech or purchases on a shopping list. However, the imagination can be used just as successfully to promote the more creative aspects of life-enrichment.

Increasing creativity

Imagine that you are someone else. Drift into a trance state, letting your mind become receptive to helpful influences as you allow yourself to forget who you are, where you are and what you are. Let your consciousness enter this someone else with whom you are identifying. Become this other person, merging with him or her, possessing the same qualities, knowledge and skills.

In this way, you may wish to merge with a present or past pianist as a means of improving your keyboard skills, or with a famous novelist to facilitate your fluency of writing, or with a painter to help you create better paintings. Should you have some knowledge of the history of music, for example, instead of identifying with another person then you may prefer to go to a particular time and place — perhaps to the home of Beethoven. There you can dwell for a few minutes of clock time, distorted so as to give you all the time that you need to learn a new composition in the style of Beethoven and to practise it so that on your return from trance you can play it. Or else, you can go into the realms of your own music, bringing back fresh ideas of your own making.

Although such identification with a composer, painter or writer, or with a particular place where an artist composed, painted, or wrote is likely to stimulate your creativity and perhaps to spark off new ideas and variations on your usual themes, do not expect to begin composing music like a Mozart, or painting like a Rembrandt, or writing like a Hemingway. However, you should notice a definite improvement in your work. Naturally, you need certain skills as a starting point, but then this fantasy of merging with great talent can provide the trigger which enables you to go beyond this basic level.

Writers, painters, musicians, and other artists have learnt to trust their imaginations to provide inspiration. Often they may sit quietly, allowing their minds to become still, as blank as possible. They provide no direction, allowing their minds to drift at will until imagery related to their work surfaces. A writer may see characters appear as clearly as if they were real people, interacting as if they were performing in a play or a film. He or she simply does not know what is going to happen. The story virtually writes itself. Musicians may see music being written before their eyes. They may hear single instruments or entire orchestras in their heads. Sometimes highly original compositions seem to have come from 'somewhere else' outside the artist. Completed works may appear full-blown to a painter before he or she has even commenced painting.

There is nothing unusual about any of this. Artists accept it as an everyday occurrence. So can we. Being confident that it will happen helps. Assuming a relaxed quiet state of body and mind does the trick, too. Permitting the mind to drift wherever the images take it helps even more.

However, if you seek to tap into the creativity of your imagination in this way, and yet you do not seem to be getting anywhere, use a stimulus. Should you wish to write a poem, introduce a few key words into your mind. Play around with them. If writing music appeals, hum a few bars and let your mind do with it what it will, perhaps imagining yourself as a famous composer.

Use television, radio, and books as vehicles to increase your enjoyment of life, infusing excitement and added interest. You can become the characters you see and read about if you allow your imagination free play. Books, in particular, allow you more scope here, if you are prepared to pause, to step back and savour the experiences provided for you. Let your imagination take you further, well beyond the author's limits. Surely this is a marvellous way of reducing boredom in your life.

Defeating boredom

This is the beauty of fantasy trips. As a result of the speed and flexibility of your imagery, you can live many lives at once, going back into the past and forward into the future. You can do anything without suffering the adverse consequences of things turning out badly. It all happens in your own private world. You can experiment with different lifestyles, just as you can visit many different places.

Singer and Switzer write of an elderly woman living in upstate New York who took daily trips in her imagination as a release from monotony and loneliness. She put it this way:

> Every afternoon I allow myself one hour or so during which I sit in an armchair and picture myself living in a villa in Florence, Italy. I see the pink-roofed house, the geraniums in the window boxes and in the clay pots along the path. I may work in the garden for a while amid the singing of the birds. Sometimes I walk down the hall to the street across the Arno River by the Ponte Vecchio and head up the hill to the Pitti Palace. I stroll through cool galleries looking at the paintings and at the lovely views of the city one sees from the palace windows. Then I meander slowly up through the Boboli Gardens to the Porcelain Museum and the panoramic view of the Tuscan hills one gets there.

Mind trips such as this can be an especially great boon to the bedridden, to anyone who is unable to move around easily, and to those lacking the financial resources to travel. It may not be as good as the real thing, but it is certainly far, far better than the nothing that many people experience when they allow themselves to slip into the depression of a monotonous daily routine from which they see no escape. Such people can do as the New York lady did. They may revisit a place that they have seen previously, or go to some place where they have never been before.

It does not take much effort. Choose a part of the world which interests you in some way. Use an atlas to find such places. Read travel books about this area. Study the photographs. Decide on a specific route taking you to the people and places you want to visit. Imagine walking or riding through the city and countryside, talking with local residents, creating little adventures for yourself.

Similarly, you can decide to live in your imagination a different life. Create imaginary personalities in other times and places. Be playful. Realize that you can turn these other personalities on and off at will. Use them either to enhance your creativity, as described in the last section, or to simply add something different so as to embellish your daily routine. Becoming a sports hero is a popular fantasy. So, too, is the fantasy of being a successful public performer, gaining adulation and applause.

Creating an alter ego may be of interest. This creation can be your opposite, behaving in ways you would never dream of, saying things you would never say, experiencing adventures you would never dare contemplate. Many an idle moment spent waiting for someone or something can be passed most agreeably in this way.

Children do it. It does not seem to harm them. Perhaps we put away 'childish things' too quickly, losing a sense of enrichment in our adult lives. Fantasy seems to be one of these things for, as well as providing the sense of fun and release which I've been writing about in this section, it can also be most useful in the more serious matter of decision-making.

Decision-making and your imagination

Though your fantasizing will be more controlled, being directed towards a specific point, it still embraces the freedom and flexibility that I have been stressing. Shirley Tulley, who conducts a small mixed business with her husband, frequently uses fantasy as an aid in making decisions.

On one occasion, Shirley had to decide whether to change houses, shifting from a neighbourhood where she had lived for many years to a 'better' suburb. Such a move is a major step. While most of the decisions that we make really do not matter, because we can usually reverse a poor choice without too much difficulty, a decision which involves the effort and expense of moving house is not one to be lightly undertaken. Shirley began by considering the worst outcome.

She asked herself: 'What would be the worst result if we left our present home and bought the house we are considering?' Her answer included losing friends, possible disintegration of a family support system, longer travelling time, and finding that she did not really like her new home. She imagined herself in the situation where all these things happened, considering all the while how she would feel.

Then, Shirley considered the situation if she remained where she was. What was the worst result that could eventuate? Here her answers revolved around increased crime rate, bad company for her children, and no opportunity to improve the family's status. Again, she used her imagination to create a vivid impression of the situation.

Having experienced the worst in her imagination,

Shirley considered the best. Her new home turned out to be marvellous, she met new friends while still retaining close family ties, her children loved their new school, and many other things turned out very well. When she thought of the best that could happen in her existing situation, Shirley realized that she could imagine little improvement on her worst scenario. Her decision was virtually made for her.

What Shirley did was mix her worst fears together with her highest hopes, allowing this blend to guide her in making a decision. By using her imagination in this way, Shirley effectively cut through the mental turmoil which is so often associated with problem-solving and decision-making.

You can follow Shirley's lead. Start with the worst situation, experiencing the anxieties, fears, and insecurities involved in this. Then, switch to the completely optimistic view. Everything will be marvellous. Finally, combine the pessimistic and optimistic scenarios into what you see as a realistic appraisal of the situation.

However, it is not only as an aid to decision-making that Shirley has reason to bless her imagination. Since she has started practising a technique which she first read about in Jean Houston's *The Possible Human*, she believes that she has been able to enrich her life through enhancing her perceptive abilities.

Improving perception

Shirley uses the power of fantasy to help lift the veils that have grown over her perceptions. To do so, she begins by closing her eyes and focusing on the evenness of her breath, becoming sensitive to this rhythm for a while. Then she imagines that she is travelling through the blood vessels of her body, transported by a little blood platelet. This takes her from the small toe on her right foot, through that foot and leg, in a great arterial channel until she reaches her pelvis. From this point, Shirley continues upward through her chest, her neck, her face, until she arrives at the cerebral cortex of her brain.

She moves to the pineal gland, or third eye, located midway between her eyes. This is supposedly the seat of inner seeing. Here she visualizes the 'House of the Senses'. In the door is a golden key on which is Shirley's name. She turns the key, opens the door, and drops the key into her pocket. As she goes inside the house, she finds in the hall all kinds of cleaning equipment — vacuum cleaners, mops, sponges, hoses, and empty garbage bags.

The room opening off the hall to the right is Shirley's 'Room of Vision'. This she imagines as having dusty corners, darkened windows, heaps of rubbish, and burnt-out light globes. It is in dire need of cleaning — which is what Shirley imagines herself doing. After scrubbing the floor, she polishes the windows and opens them, removes the dusty curtains, and removes the accumulated rubbish. Once she has done so, she looks out the window of her light-filled room, gazing for miles in every direction at a world washed clean, bright, and shining.

At the end of this room is a locked door. Shirley opens it with her golden key. She leaves the door open as she goes into her 'Room of Hearing'. This, too, is a mess, with cobwebs everywhere, dust, and debris on walls and floor. Again, Shirley imagines herself cleaning up, scrubbing, polishing. She even expands the size of the room, pushing back the walls, making the ceiling higher, believing that as she takes these actions she is improving the quality of her hearing. She knows that this is so because once the cleaning is complete, she walks around her large airy room, listening to her footsteps echoing on the floor, hearing the 'swoosh' of the fresh air as it sweeps in through the open window to blow away any remaining dust. At the open window, Shirley hears the wind stirring in the trees, the singing of the birds, and the laughter of children at play.

The process continues. A 'Room of Smell' opens off

the 'Room of Hearing'. A 'Room of Taste' opens off the 'Room of Smell'. Shirley cleans these in the same way so that her senses of smell and taste become sharper. She can enjoy the lovely fragrance blown in by the wind, together with the tang of salt on her tongue.

The 'Room of Touch' comes next. All the sludge and refuse is thrown out until the room becomes vibrant with life. Then Shirley can enjoy the feel of the wooden window frame, the caress of the breeze on her cheek, and the rough texture of the carpet under her feet.

Finally, Shirley returns to the hall where all the rubbish has been dumped, ready for removal. A staircase leads to the floor above. Shirley mounts this staircase. She finds herself in a large room, the 'Room of the Sixth Sense'. In this room reside all the senses not encountered on the ground floor. It needs cleaning too. Once she has finished doing so, Shirley walks out on a balcony which leads off this room. From it, she can look down on the Rooms of Sight, Hearing, Smell, Taste and Touch. All these newly cleaned rooms are connected by the doors which Shirley has left open.

Shirley becomes aware of a gentle, warm breeze blowing through the open windows and doors of her senses. Lifting up her head, she deeply inhales the fresh air of the 'Room of the Sixth Sense', and then, swinging her head down, she exhales, blowing air through all five rooms. This she does several times, before relaxing and enjoying a sensation of intense aliveness, together with an increased awareness of mind and body. Returning down the stairs to the front hall, Shirley collects the garbage, takes it outside to a large incinerator, burns it until nothing remains; and, in shutting the door of the house, she leaves it all behind, returning to her everyday awareness.

This procedure takes longer to describe than it actually takes to go through it. Shirley uses it occasionally, when the world seems flat and dull. This is because, when she returns from the House of the Senses, she notices changes in her perception. The objects she sees seem brighter, more clearly defined, sounds are crisper, her taste buds more discerning, her senses of smell and touch more sensitive. The world seems a generally brighter place, and she is able to lift herself to a fresh appreciation of her surroundings, sloughing off the flatness and the dullness. Thus, she enriches her life.

There are so many ways of enriching your life through the use of your imagination. Some have been touched on in this chapter. Another way is so important that it deserves a chapter all to itself.

13 Sexual Fantasy

The value of sexual fantasy

It is easy to feel guilty when we fantasize about sex. Probably this is because of our early conditioning when fear and guilt were used as a means of keeping us from doing those things which our elders believed were 'bad'. Unfortunately, we carry these childhood fears and guilts into our adult lives, often quite inappropriately. They can block us from a full enjoyment of our lives. Nowhere is this more apparent than in the sensitive area of sex.

Books such as those written by Nancy Friday, *My Secret Garden* and *Men in love*, have made sexual fantasy more legitimate. Instead of feeling guilty about the fact that they have all kinds of erotic imagery while engaging in sexual intercourse, men and women are realizing that such fantasizing is an acceptable way of enhancing their sexual pleasure. Many couples with an impoverished sex life have found new vitality through the use of imagery such as that described by Nancy Friday.

In her books, she reports on the results of her surveys of people's sexual imagery. This can be very helpful to individuals who do not realize that their fantasies of rape, of having sex with many partners, and of anal and oral sex are not signs of a twisted and deprived mind but are, in fact, quite normal. They are shared by many other people. Just because a person imagines being raped or raping another does not mean that she or he wants to act in this way. It simply is a means of using fantasy to heighten sexual enjoyment in a way that inflicts harm on no one.

I recall a patient whom I will call Susan Bates. She felt most uneasy about her inability to concentrate on her husband during sexual relations. Though she loved him greatly, Susan was unable to achieve orgasm unless she fantasized a particular situation. In it, she was abducted from her home by a group of men who took her to a house well out in the country. She was then raped repeatedly by these men. Always, when she imagined herself being treated in this way, she would achieve orgasm quickly and repeatedly.

Susan was reassured when I had her read of other women who enjoyed very similar fantasies, using them as triggers to similarly achieve sexual fulfilment. She was further reassured when I told her of other patients who regularly employed erotic imagery far more 'outrageous' in content. Thus, Susan was able to continue using her imagination in a way that led to fulfilment without the unnecessary burden of guilt.

Though she developed other fantasies, her forcible abduction and rape visualization remained her favourite. We all tend to develop such 'old friends'. These 'sure-fire' arousal triggers can be relied on to produce the effect that we want, removing any barriers to excitement which may exist in the real world. In our imagination, we are not bound by restrictions. There are no limits in terms of stamina, attractiveness, legalities, or moral codes. All we need is the creativity to give birth to a fantasy, nourishing it, modifying it, and enjoying it so that it can bring about an instantaneous surge of passion.

That most of us do make use of such fantasy is indicated by the many research studies conducted into this aspect of human functioning. Of people interviewed, something like 70 per cent of women and 90 per cent of men claimed to use sexual imagery while engaged in relationships with their partners. Such fantasies included being with a different lover or lovers, of being in bed with a famous person, usually a film star, and of being forced into sexual intercourse.

Sexual therapy

The prevalence of such fantasizing is used by therapists as one means of helping their patients achieve a more satisfactory sex life. Through fantasy, both men and women can overcome various blocks and problems. Many of these arise because one or both partners over-concentrate on the actual physical sensations which they experience in their genitals, attempting to increase these sensations as if they were in some kind of competition. A performance anxiety can develop through focusing attention in this way, so much so that a man may be unable to maintain an erection or a woman may be unable to achieve orgasm. It is almost as if people with this problem 'stand outside' themselves, watching and judging, usually negatively, the way they perform.

Fantasies can distract from such watching and judging. It enables men, in particular, to adjust their level of sexual excitement to that of their partner. If they should want to slow down, they may visualize non-erotic scenes such as playing sport, reading stock exchange figures, or having a beer with a friend. In this way they can delay their own orgasm until their partner is ready. Conversely, a man may use erotic imagery to 'speed up' if his partner is approaching her climax and he wants to enjoy a simultaneous orgasm.

Woody Allen expresses this beautifully in the film *Play it Again, Sam*. His best friend's wife, with whom he has gone to bed for the first time, inquires why he kept calling 'slide . . . slide' while he was making love. Woody explains that he was thinking of baseball because it 'keeps me going'. Of course, the overemphasis placed upon the simultaneous orgasm is, in itself, a prime cause of performance anxiety. Though two people climaxing together can be intensely satisfying, there is no reason why this must always be the goal. There are many other ways of achieving sexual pleasure and such ways may be more readily explored when the necessity of the simultaneous orgasm is dispensed with. If it happens, that's great; if not, it does not really matter.

Sexual anxieties and performance difficulties may often be overcome by imagery focused on the pleasure of sex. On other occasions, emphasis may be more fruitfully directed towards imagery designed to help people overcome specific problems.

Common sexual problems

When lack of *sexual desire* is the problem, our old friend the control knob can be useful. With this control regulating a one-to-ten scale, sexual desire may be increased by turning the knob and going up through the numbers. As you see each number, you concentrate on feeling an increase in sexual desire.

Or, during masturbation, focus on any erotic stimulus which you find arousing. For men, masturbation fantasies are likely to include intercourse with a stranger, group sex, and forcing someone to have sex. Women are more likely to fantasize acts in which they would never actually engage, particularly in the context of being forced to have sex. This theme of being sexually dominated is very popular with females. So during masturbation, just before the point of orgasm, the idea is to switch away from the erotic imagery to focus on sexual interaction with your partner. On subsequent occasions, this switch to fantasies of your partner is to occur earlier and earlier in the masturbatory sequence. By doing so, you increase the possibility of your sexual partner eliciting the excitement and pleasure previously associated with the erotic fantasy.

This same conditioning procedure may then be applied to sexual interaction with your partner. Begin by fantasizing arousing erotic scenes, focus on that fantasy during the preliminary stages of sexual intercourse and, as orgasm approaches, switch your attention to thoughts of the present reality.

Imagery can sometimes help with *vaginismus*, too. By focusing on your pelvic area, you will be able to describe the tension you feel, the tightness that makes intercourse so difficult. Often you will be able to capture that feeling in a single image, probably the most common one being that of a tight knot. Visualize the easing of that tension so that you see the knot unravelling. Perhaps you might imagine a rope with a knot in it, which gradually loosens until it disappears completely.

An earlier technique, that of describing the tension in terms of its size, shape, colour, and texture, may be helpful with such a problem. By reducing the size to nothing, or by changing the shape, or colour, or texture, you may be able to change your experience of the tension, either by reducing it to manageable proportions or by causing it to disappear entirely.

Impotency in males is frequently the result of the performance anxiety mentioned earlier in this chapter. Each sexual encounter is seen as a challenge, a performance at which they might not succeed. This anxiety, this fear of failure, intensifies the likelihood of failure. Therefore, the use of distracting erotic fantasy is one way in which impotence may be overcome. So, too, is the recall of a previously satisfying sexual experience — as a means of training yourself to gain and maintain an erection.

Practise this in the relaxed trance state. Imagine that you have already had a pleasurable and successful sexual experience which has been filmed. You have seen the film before. Now you are seeing it again. In great detail it shows you and your partner enjoying sexual activity to the full. It is highly erotic, for in this film you are playing out your own fantasy. Your erection is effortless and powerful, maintained as you would wish. This film is yours, to be run as often as you want, whenever you want. If you desire, every time you see it you can 'get into' the 'you' that is on the screen, experiencing the erotic feelings, the powerful erection. And every time you do so, you are providing your unconscious mind with an experience of sexual success.

Fantasizing a successful sexual experience can be helpful if the problem is *premature ejaculation*. Often the cause of this sexual difficulty is that the man is frightened that he will lose his erection before he can have intercourse. Therefore, he shortens foreplay and attempts penetration before his erection is really firm enough. So, again, it can be helpful if the man visualizes himself maintaining his erection and completing intercourse successfully. As with other applications of fantasy, it may be valuable to imagine an admired model achieving the desired sexual success if self-visualization is difficult to achieve.

Some useful fantasies

Sharing sexual fantasies can be helpful in heightening the enjoyment of both parties. Often, we are reluctant to reveal our fantasies to our sexual partner, perhaps because we feel that they may seem offensive or that our partner will be upset if we are thinking of some one else rather than him or her. Yet, once people realize how widespread such use of fantasy is, they may be more ready to tell of their imagery, knowing that their partner probably also uses this method of sexual arousal.

Fantasy and imagination can really be invaluable in enriching your sex life through the variety and enjoyment which it adds to it. However, as with all the fantasies described in this book, it is important to realize the difference between dreams and reality. In most cases, it is desirable to act out the fantasy inside your head rather than doing so in the real world. On occasions, though, couples will act out their fantasies, playing a variety of sexual games. This is one big advantage of sharing imagined erotic stimuli for, should both parties have comparable fantasies, it becomes much easier to translate them into reality.

Though most sexual imagery concerns the actual act of

intercourse in one form or another, other fantasies may be of a different kind. For example, Susan Bates, the lady mentioned earlier in this chapter, imagines a trip through her genital area. She sees herself inside her vagina, checking every detail of this beautiful chamber, feeling its entrance, roof and walls, dwelling on any 'special points' which respond with pleasant sensations. Susan, by this means, has located areas which respond with pleasure to touch, tapping, rubbing, or to pressure.

In these areas, she visualizes pleasure as 'a thing'. This can vary. Sometimes it is a colour. On other occasions, it may be a sound, a sensation, a perfume, a taste, or any combination of these. Whatever 'the thing' may be, Susan lingers on it, increasing and diminishing it at will. By exercising this control, she can intensify her enjoyment during sexual activity with her husband, imagining the stimulation which various pleasure points are receiving.

Susan's husband, Steve, also uses his imagination to heighten his sexual enjoyment. He focuses on his testicles and penis, imagining them becoming fully alive, increasing their sensitivity as if he is turning up the volume of a radio. As he does so, he feels a pulse beat there which he can slow down or speed up at will. This pulse beat represents the forces of life flowing through his body, focusing itself in his testicles and penis during times of sexual excitement. Blood flow to the genital area is increased through the use of this fantasy and, as sexual arousal is basically a blood flow phenomenon, it is no wonder that Steve is able to heighten his sexual pleasure.

Just as the imagination can enrich our lives sexually, it can also enhance our enjoyment of sport, for we do tend to enjoy those things that we do well. Doing well at sport is something that can be assisted quite powerfully through the use of the imagination, as we shall see in the final chapter.

14 Improving Sports Performance

Images, not words

Our literate society places great emphasis on words. This is how we learn. Yet, experience tells us that words are not always the best path to learning. In his book, *Inner Tennis*, Tim Gallwey tells the story of his first attempt to teach non-verbally. He told the lad whom he was coaching that he was not going to tell him what to do. Instead, he wanted him to watch what he, Gallwey, did as he hit the tennis ball, and to do the same thing himself. The boy watched and said: 'I see what you're doing. You transfer your weight from your back foot to your front foot as you hit the ball'. He then proceeded to copy Gallwey's stroke, doing everything right *except* transfering his weight.

Gallwey has provided many other examples which indicate that, at least in the area of tennis, words may be a quite ineffective vehicle for teaching and learning. In *The Centered Skier* Denise McCluggage makes the same point:

> As you ski, attend to the images, not the words ... learn to translate instructor's words into images and forebear converting images to words — hastening to put every experience into a jar and labelling it ... Use your left brained logic to figure out exactly what point the instruction is trying to make, then search your own experience to come up with a metaphor that makes a connection and

159

animates the point for you. 'Oh I see, you mean sort of *melt* the downhill knee'.

Images appear to be the most effective way of communicating with the unconscious mind, of showing it what we want. They are probably of far more use than relying solely on positive thinking, which has serious limitations as a means of improving sports performance. In the book which I referred to earlier, Gallwey makes the point that when you concentrate on slogans such as 'I will win', you also embrace the possibility that the opposite can happen — that 'I will lose'. Positive thinking can easily, then, become negative thinking in that it creates more fears than it dissipates: 'I will make this 10-foot putt', but also perhaps 'I will miss this 10-foot putt'. It is difficult to concentrate solely on the positive, putting the negative out of your mind.

I do not, however, want to belittle positive thinking. It is certainly far more helpful to approach any sporting performance expecting success than it is to expect failure. However, we have tended to overemphasize its power. Positive thinking alone will not make you a winner. This has been demonstrated repeatedly by studies into the 'psyching-up' process, particularly with football players. The 'rah-rah, go out and kill them' approach so favoured by coaches often generates a pressure on players that interferes with performance, possibly adding to their anxieties about winning. It has been suggested, in fact, that players who perform well do so despite this 'psyching-up' rather than because of it. 'Psyching-up' is done with words, exhortations, pleas, appeals to players' pride. Images of success are likely to produce more impressive results.

The concept of mental playing

McCluggage provides a number of examples which effectively illustrate how sportsmen and women use images to 'play' their sport. She tells of the **BMW** racing car team sitting in silence, 'driving a particular course, mentally practising their lines through the turns and their shift points. As each raises his hand to signal the completion of a lap, the team manager uses a stop watch to note the time taken. It is interesting that the times done in the head are similar to those actually done on the track.'

During a basketball game, a player receives a free throw. He concentrates his gaze on the flat ellipse that is the entry to the basket's netting. When he 'sees' the ball there, 'flowing over the rim like a leaf riding a torrent down a drainpipe', he makes his shot, launching the ball on the stream to follow its image.

The skier replays in her mind her last run, one in which she fell. She visualizes this fall, seeing herself leave her weight shift too late into the turn and her ski tips crossing. Then, she reverses the mental film, returning to the point where the offending sequence began. This time she imagines the timely transfer of weight, the pole plant, the successful execution of the turn. She does this as she returns up the slope on the chair lift. What she has done is eliminate her error, replacing it with the image of success. She is now ready to approach her next run with confidence.

On the practice tee the golfer pauses after each drive, closes his eyes, and watches a replay of his last shot. His muscles replay it faithfully. He detects his error as he sees his shoulders unwinding ahead of his hips. Now, he has clear feedback on what he needs to do to improve his swing.

Many sporting champions claim to 'play mentally'. Golfers such as Jack Nicklaus and Gary Player have described how, before they actually play a stroke, they first visualize the ball landing where they want it to land, seeing the bounce, the arc of the ball in flight, the swing, and the ball leaving the ground. Then they link these images in the proper sequence, visualizing the swing, the ball's trajectory, its landing and bouncing to the selected spot.

In the tennis world, Chris Evert is reputed to mentally rehearse a forthcoming match, centring her attention on anticipating an opponent's strategy and style. She then visualizes herself countering with her own attack to overcome this strategy and style. She carries such a rehearsal out in a relaxed state in order to enhance the vividness of the imagery.

Mental rehearsal

Although the concept of 'mental playing' of a sport may be analyzed into several separate components, what is usually meant by the term is mental rehearsal. This is illustrated by Chris Evert's pre-match imagery and Jack Nicklaus' visualization of his shot before he hits it. These players always mentally rehearse the correct action, imagining the successful play. To mentally rehearse a mistake is to reinforce the wrong actions, with all the negative emotions that accompany them. The golfer who, before he swings, concentrates on avoiding the sand trap is actually focusing on what he must not do, preparing his body to perform just those actions which he wants to avoid. Similarly, the tennis player who thinks he must not hit the ball to the man at the net will then do just that. He has mentally rehearsed a mistake. So, focus on what you want to do and mentally rehearse only the desired action.

Rehearse how you make the successful play, whether it be shooting for goal, stroking a tennis ball, running a race, or using a golf putter. Mentally go over the correct motions and strategies. Do this many times. In this way you overlearn the response, conditioning your unconscious mind to produce it automatically when you are under pressure.

In *Sports Psyching*, Tutko and Tosi provide a detailed schedule as a guide to mental rehearsal. Five steps are involved.

- *Study the pictures.* Get a set of photos or drawings of a particular play which you want to practise. If these are unavailable, write down the parts of the play in as much detail as possible. However, the words will not provide as useful a guide as the pictures.
- *Imagine the sequence in slow motion.* Close your eyes and imagine yourself going through the same sequence in slow motion. Note the crucial components at each stage of the action. How are your feet positioned? What are your legs doing? Your hips? Where is your head? How is your grip? Imagine, in your body, the sensations involved, how each part is feeling. Visualize the play itself. See where, for example, the ball goes from the start to the end.
- *Study and imagine the sequence again.* Look at the pictures or the list a second time. Have you missed anything? Have you got something wrong? If so, correct it. Go through the action again in slow motion with your eyes closed.
- *Repeat the sequence five times in more detail.* Mentally replay the procedure in slow motion. Open your eyes. Recheck your pictures or list. Repeat the procedure in even more detail. Check again. Do this five times. When you can go slowly through the action, start to finish, in detail without error, then you have conditioned your mind very effectively. This may take a number of mental rehearsals so do not pressure yourself that you must get it right first time.
- *Image the sequence at normal speed 10 times.* Close your eyes. Imagine yourself going through the play at normal speed. It is the best you have ever performed. Open your eyes and check over the reminders. Go through the play again. Congratulate yourself on a terrific play. Repeat this 10 times.

Though this seems a rather time-consuming process, once you get the hang of it, it can usually be done in about 10 minutes. Many sportsmen and women have found it to be time well spent. Studies of chess players, for example, have shown that champions do not necessarily visualize the board better than lesser players. They do not appear to have significantly better memories either. However, the better players have repeatedly practised, both in their minds and in actuality, hundreds of moves and countermoves. They have tried out every strategy, every position, every move and countermove so many times that when confronted with a problem situation during a match, they respond almost instinctively, making the appropriate countermove which they have overlearned through practice. Much of this practice has been mental. They may play this right move quickly, apparently without deep thought. Deep thought is not necessary. The pattern has been absorbed unconsciously, ready to be produced under match pressure.

A golfing friend of mine, Peter Waterman, has done something similar with his putting. At one time it was the weakest part of his game, but it is now his strongest feature. He has visualized himself putting successfully so often that his mental rehearsal has prepared him to putt accurately under match conditions. Peter has helped himself somewhat by also imagining the hole becoming bigger and bigger as he lines up his putt. By the time he strokes the ball, the hole is so large that he feels he cannot miss. He has imagined this happening so often that, when actually playing a round, he sees the hole getting bigger without him really trying to make it appear so.

Peter has also used another mental 'trick' to assist his play. When he mentally rehearses an entire round, which is what he does before a match, he imagines playing each hole as if it is the first. That is, he starts fresh each time. By inculcating this idea in his mental rehearsal, he has been able to carry it over virtually automatically to his actual play. It takes off a lot of pressure, because each problem carries a past and a future. By eliminating the past and changing the future, Peter has changed two-thirds of his problem. By thinking about each hole as being the first, he has no anxiety from the past. He has also changed the future to one of positive expectancy.

Pre-game warm-up routine

Peter plays an imaginary round as a warm-up. Tutko and Tosi suggest a more complex, five-step procedure as a way of preparing for competition. This routine can take anything from three minutes to twenty minutes, depending on how much time you want to devote to it. It can be done in the locker room, sitting on a bench, or waiting on the sports arena:

- *Getting loose.* Briefly tense your legs, buttocks, thighs, stomach, back, neck, arms, shoulders, jaw, face, and eye muscles. Tense each muscle, briefly hold the tension, then tell it to 'let go'.
- *Breathing easy.* Inhale, hold your breath while counting to four, then slowly exhale saying to yourself 'Easy ... easy ... easy'. This can be repeated two to five times.
- *Staying on the ball.* Look at an object which you have adopted as an object of concentration. The tennis player might use a tennis ball, the basket-baller the rim of a basket, the baseballer or cricketer could use a bat, the athlete his or her spikes, and so on. While concentrating on this object, repeat its name over and over again, 'Ball ... ball ... ball', or 'bat ... bat ... bat'. Maintain this concentration for a munute.
- *Mental rehearsal.* Close your eyes. In your mind, picture the upcoming plays which you expect to make. In slow motion, see yourself accomplishing them successfully. Though you cannot anticipate everything that will happen, rehearse the fundamental moves.

• *Body rehearsal.* You may prefer to do this in private before you go on to the playing arena, or it can take place on the field or court when you do your physical warm-up. Pretend that you are shadow-boxing. Go through the basic moves, first with eyes closed, then with eyes open, one set in slow motion, one at normal speed.

Mental rehearsal can be very valuable indeed. However, it can only help you if you have already learned the basic skills. You have to know what you are rehearsing. If you do not know the right thing to do, you can hardly practise doing it either actually or mentally. All you will do is rehearse your errors. Once you have the necessary basic skill, then mental rehearsal will accelerate your performance beyond that which is possible with physical practice alone.

This is indicated by an experiment involving three groups of children who had learned the basic skill of skipping. Each group was treated differently. One continued regular skipping practice. A second did no further physical practice but repeatedly went through the steps mentally. The other group practised neither physically nor mentally, doing activities unrelated to rope jumping. All three groups were tested several weeks later. Group one did best. However, those of group two who practised mentally did nearly as well, and were much better than group three.

Remaking your movie

Mental rehearsal may be described as running movies in your mind. This can involve the procedures outlined in the last section. It can be as simple as remembering the details of your best sporting performance — how you felt and what you did — and running it repeatedly through the projector of your mind. If football is your sport, you see your best kicks, passes, and tackles so that your unconscious mind is conditioned to repeat these in every game which you play.

You can also remake your movies. Without realizing it, we continually replay a mental film of those previous sporting performances in which we did poorly. This saps our confidence. It also programs our unconscious mind to produce the same errors again. McCluggage describes in *The Centered Skier* an exercise which is designed to overcome this tendency through the recutting of childhood movies.

Her group stretched out on the floor, relaxed the tension in their bodies, attended to easy breathing, and settled into a receptive state. She asked them to remember a sporting incident from their childhood — one of miserable failure. Perhaps they had let down their team, finished a long last in a race, or been thrashed in a tennis match.

McCluggage asked her participants to play through their movie of this disastrous failure slowly, re-experiencing again whatever they had felt at the time. Usually this was disappointment, dismay, disgust, anger, frustration, and other negative emotions. Then she suggested that they replay the movie, cutting in new footage to transform disaster into triumph. This time they save the team, surge past other runners to win the race, and play superb tennis to win the tennis match comfortably. As participants remade the movie, they were asked to experience the feelings that went with this success, to enjoy the elation of winning.

It *is* possible to go back into the past in order to turn failure into success. It is also possible to use do-it-yourself desensitization to remove the fear which has been engendered by past failure. Often an athlete who has been injured retains a fear of further injury, thus preventing top performance. I know of a number of high-divers with this problem. Perhaps they have left the high tower awkwardly, hitting the water hard. The memory of this pain reduces their confidence. Their diving becomes more tentative, and they are increasingly likely to repeat the painful performance.

One of these divers, Lyn Ross, used systematic desensitization very successfully to overcome her fear and to remake the movie of a particularly awkward dive which she had kept rerunning in her mind. The hierarchy Lynn constructed for herself was as follows:

- Hearing a radio report on the results of a diving competition
- Seeing a magazine picture of a girl poised on a low diving board
- Overhearing people talking about the height of a high-diving tower
- Attending a diving competition as a spectator
- Standing at the bottom of the ladder leading to the diving platform
- Standing at the back of the diving platform.
- Walking into position, ready to dive
- Being poised on the edge of the platform
- Leaving the board, diving through the air, and entering the water smoothly.

In a relaxed state, Lyn imagined the first of these scenes When she could do so without any trace of anxiety, she moved on to the next one. Should she feel anxious, she would switch her thoughts to her breathing rhythm, flowing with it until she became calm. Then she would go back to her hierarchy. It did not take long before she was imagining, without any trace of anxiety, herself diving from the high tower.

Fears of all sorts can be overcome through the use of our imagination. In so many other ways, too, we have seen how fantasy can enrich our lives, giving us a feeling of increased control and enjoyment. Imagination may be a double-edged sword, but, used positively, it can often transform our lives. I hope that through the ideas contained in these pages you will be able to effect this transformation for yourself.

References

Ahsen, A. *Psycheye,* Brandon House, New York, 1977.

Bandler, R. and Grinder, J. *Frogs into Princes,* Real People Press, Moab, Utah, 1979.

Clavell, J. *Shogun*, Hodder & Stoughton, London, 1975.

Friday, N. *My Secret Garden: Woman's sexual fantasies,* Pocket Books, New York, 1973.

Friday, N. *Men in Love: Their secret fantasies,* Arrow Books, London, 1980.

Gallwey, T. *Inner Tennis,* Random House, New York, 1976.

Gibbons, D. *Beyond Hypnosis : Explorations in hyperempiria,* Power Publishing Company, South Orange, N.J., 1973.

Gibbons, D. E. *Applied Hypnosis and Hyperempiria,* Plenum Press, New York, 1979.

Grinder, J. and Bandler, R. *Trance-formations*, Real People Press, Moab, Utah, 1981.

Houston, J. *The Possible Human*, J. P. Tarcher, Los Angeles, 1982.

Jaffe, D. T. *Healing From Within*, Alfred A. Knopf, New York, 1980.

Jencks, B. *Respiration for Relaxation, Invigoration and Special Accomplishments,* Jenks, Utah, 1974.

Joy, B. *Joy's Way*, J. P. Tarcher, Los Angeles, 1979.

Luthe, W. (ed.) *Autogenic Therapy,* Grune and Stratton, New York, 1967.

McCluggage, D. *The Centered Skier,* Vermont Cross-roads Press, Waitsfield, Vermont, 1977.

Morris, F. *Hypnosis with Friends and Lovers,* Harper and   Row, San Francisco, 1979.

Phillips, A. *Transformational Psychology,* Elsevier, New York, 1981.

Rhinehart, L. *The Book of EST,* Sphere, London, 1976.

Sheikh, A. A. and Shaefer, J. T. (eds.) *The Potential of Fantasy and Imagination,* Brandon House, New York, 1979.

Shorr, J.E. *Psycho-imagination Therapy,* Intercontinental Medical Book Company, New York, 1972.

Singer, T. J. and Switzer, E. *Mind Play,* Prentice-Hall, Englewood Cliffs, N.J., 1980.

Stanton, H. E. *The Plus Factor: A Guide to Positive Living,* Fontana/Collins, Sydney, 1979.

Stanton, H. E. *The Healing Factor: A Guide to Positive Health,* Fontana/Collins, Sydney, 1981.

Stanton, H. E. *The Stress Factor: A Guide to More Relaxed Living,* Fontana/Collins, Sydney, 1983.

Torry, E. F. *The Mind Game,* Emerson Hall, New York, 1972.

Tutko, T. and Tosi, U. *Sports Psyching,* J. P. Tarcher, Los Angeles, 1976.

Weatherhead, L. D. *Psychology, Religion and Healing,* Hodder & Stoughton, London, 1952.

Index

About the Author

After graduating from Melbourne University, Dr Stanton spent eight years teaching in secondary schools and five years lecturing in teacher training colleges. He has taught in the universities of South Australia and Tasmania since 1969, and is now Consultant on Higher Education at the University of Tasmania. He also runs a consultancy service for companies and the public sector, and has a private practice in clinical and sports psychology.

Dr Stanton is author of the following books, also published by Optima:

The Plus Factor: A Guide to Positive Living (February 1988)
The Healing Factor: A Guide to Positive Health (February 1988)
The Stress Factor: A Guide to More Relaxed Living (August 1988)